James Bryant Conant has distinguished himself in four careers. For almost twenty years he was a research scientist in chemistry. In 1933, he accepted the presidency of Harvard University and turned his attention to educational administration. After twenty years at Harvard, Dr. Conant served as United States High Commissioner of Germany and, later, as Ambassador to that country. In 1957, with the aid of a grant from the Carnegie Foundation, he began a special study of education in America. Several books have resulted from the study, the most recent of which was *The Education of American Teachers*. Dr. Conant's next book will be called *Shaping Educational Policies*.

ABOUT THE EDITOR

Ruth Nanda Anshen, philosopher and editor, plans and edits *The Credo Series*, as well as *World Perspectives, Religious Perspectives*, and the *Science of Culture Series*. She writes and lectures widely on the relationship of knowledge to the meaning of existence.

THE CREDO SERIES

VOLUMES ALREADY PUBLISHED

THE TORCH OF LIFE:
Continuity in Living Experience
BY RENÉ DUBOS

OLD WINE, NEW BOTTLES:
A Humanist Teacher at Work
BY MOSES HADAS

MAN, NATURE AND GOD:
A Quest for Life's Meaning
BY F. S. C. NORTHROP

BEYOND THE CHAINS OF ILLUSION:
My Encounter with Marx and Freud
BY ERICH FROMM

THE CHALLENGE OF THE PASSING YEARS:
My Encounter with Time
BY R. M. MACIVER

THE ANATOMY OF LIBERTY:
The Rights of Man Without Force
BY WILLIAM O. DOUGLAS

TWO MODES OF THOUGHT:
My Encounters with Science and Education
BY JAMES BRYANT CONANT

THE CREDO SERIES

PLANNED AND EDITED BY
RUTH NANDA ANSHEN

TWO MODES OF THOUGHT

My Encounters with Science and Education

BY

JAMES BRYANT CONANT

A TRIDENT PRESS BOOK
NEW YORK 1964

Prepared under the supervision of
POCKET BOOKS, INC.

LIBRARY OF CONGRESS CATALOG NUMBER: 64-18874
PUBLISHED SIMULTANEOUSLY IN THE UNITED STATES AND CANADA BY TRIDENT PRESS
MANUFACTURED IN THE UNITED STATES OF AMERICA

CONTENTS

THE CREDO SERIES

Its Meaning and Function

The Credo Series suggests that an epoch has come to an end, an epoch in which our best knowledge has been dimmed with boredom or darkened by destruction. We have felt for too long that this must be the very nature of life; this is the way life is, and to such a degree that life has consented to shrink from its own terrors, leading us to a deep apostasy of the heart and a crucifixion of our natural aspiration for experience and growth.

The absolute has surrendered to the relative. Our era of relativity, however, whether in science or in morals, does not allow us to assume that relativity implies an absence of ground to stand on, and therefore a relaxation of all effort toward foundations. "There is no firm ground," the dominant malaise of our time, this acceptance of nonfinality, summons us to a heightened task. For the failure of formulated absolutes leaves the absolute requirement to evaluate again that uncaptured reality which contains and guides the total meaning of our existence.

The Credo Series hopes to unlock a consciousness that at first sight may seem to be remote but is proved on acquaintance to be surprisingly immediate since it shows the need to reconcile the life of action with the life of contemplation, practice with principle, thought with feeling, knowledge with being, and work, no longer a form of punishment as in the Judaeo-Christian tradition, but accepted as a way toward the growth and realization of the self in all its plenitude. For the whole meaning of self lies within the observer and its shadow is cast naturally on the object observed. The fragmentation of man from his work, the being of man into an eternal and temporal half, results in an estrangement of man from his creative source, from his fellows and from himself.

The symbol of *The Credo Series* is the Eye of Osiris. It is the inner Eye. Man sees in two ways: with his physical eyes, in an empirical sensing or *seeing* by direct observation, and also by an indirect envisaging. He possesses in addition to his two sensing eyes a single, image-making, spiritual and intellectual Eye. And it is the *in-sight* of this inner Eye that purifies and makes sacred our understanding of the nature of things; for that which was shut fast has been opened by the command of the inner Eye. And we become aware that to believe is to see.

Thus, it is suggested, there may be born a sharpened vision, which comes from seeing reality as the incarnation of associations and affinities with something beyond the visible self. For it is our hope to show the human relevance of ideas, the ways in which knowledge can help us to live in the immediate and real world by pointing to the confluence of man and his vocation, of subject and object, by reverencing the curious and mysterious metabolism between man and matter, the sacred nexus between the person and his work, and by asking whether the freedom now released through the creative energies of mankind will bring salvation or destruction, the answer to which will depend upon the aims we cherish.

The Credo Series submits that the universe itself is a vast entity where man will be lost if it does not converge in the person; for material forces or energies, or impersonal ideals, or scientifically objectified learning are meaningless without their relevance for human life and their power to disclose, even in the dark tendencies of man's nature, a law transcending man's arbitrariness.

For the personal is a far higher category than the abstract universal. Personality itself is an emotional, not an intellectual, experience, and the greatest achievement of knowledge is to combine the personal within a larger unity, just as in the higher stages of development the parts that make up the whole acquire greater and greater independence and individuality within the context of the whole. Reality itself is the harmony which gives to the component particulars of a thing the equilibrium of the whole. And while physical observations are ordered with direct reference to the experimental conditions, we have in sensate experience to do with separate observations whose correlation can only be indicated by their belonging to the wholeness of mind.

It is our endeavor to show that man has reached a

turning point in consciousness, that his relationship with his creative self demands a clarification that can widen and deepen his understanding of the nature of reality. Work is made for man, not man for work. This Series hopes to demonstrate the sacramental character of work which is more easily achieved when the principal objects of our attention have taken on a symbolic form that is generally recognized and accepted: in other words, when there is an established iconography relating to the meaningful interpretation of man and his vocation. This suggests a "law" in the relationship of a person and his chosen discipline: that it is valuable only when the spiritual, the creative, life is strong enough to insist on some expression through symbols. For no work can be based on material, technological or physical aspirations alone.

The human race is now entering upon a new phase of evolutionary progress, a phase in which, impelled by the forces of evolution itself, it must converge upon itself and convert itself into one single human organism dominated by a reconciliation of knowing and being in their inner unity and destined to make a qualitative leap into a higher form of consciousness that would transcend and complement individual consciousness as we know it, or otherwise destroy itself. For the entire universe is one vast field, potential for incarnation, and achieving incandescence here and there of reason and spirit. What to some is mystery and inscrutability, to others symbolizes and declares the very nature of the cosmic process. And in the whole world of *quality* with which category by the nature of our minds we necessarily make contact, we here and there apprehend pre-eminent value. This can be achieved only if we recognize that we are unable to focus our attention on the particulars of a whole without diminishing our comprehension of the whole, and of course conversely, we can focus on the whole only by diminishing our comprehension of the particulars which constitute the whole.

This Series is designed to present a kind of intellectual autobiography of each author, to portray the nature and meaning of the creative process for the creator and to show the relevance of his work to the feelings and aspirations of the man of flesh and bone. This Series endeavors to reflect also the influence of the work on the man and on society and to point to the freedom, or lack of freedom, to choose and pursue one profession rather than another. It attempts to emphasize that the creator in any realm must surrender himself to a passionate pursuit of the hidden meaning of his labors, guided by deep personal intimations of an as yet undiscovered reality.

These volumes endeavor to indicate that it is impossible to know what constitutes a good society unless we know what defines a good individual. The self is determined by the values according to which it subordinates and integrates the rest of its values. If the values be transient, so is the self. If the values be dispersed and incoherent, so is the self. If they are organic and integrated, so is the self. The unity of human personality is its soundness. The unified self cannot be understood in terms of its constituent parts as dissected away from each other. So that finally what we see and what we do are no more and no less than what we are.

It is the effort of *The Credo Series* to define the new reality in which the estrangement of man and his work, resulting in the self-estrangement in man's existence, is overcome. This new reality is born through the reconciliation of what a man *knows* with what a man *is*. Being itself in all its presuppositions and implications can only be understood through the totality, through wholeness. St. Paul, who, like Isaiah before him, went into the market place not to secularize truth but to proclaim it, taught man that the "new creation" could be explained only by conquering the daemonic cleavages, the destructive split, in soul and cosmos. And that fragmentation always destroys a unity, produces a tearing away from the source and thereby creates disunity and isolation. The fruit can never be separated from the tree. The Tree of Life can never be disjoined from the Tree of Knowledge for both have *one and the same* root. And if man allows himself to fall into isolation, if he seeks to maintain a self segregated from the totality of which he is a necessary part, if he chooses to remain asunder, unrelated to the original context of all created things in which he too has his place—including his own labors—then this act of apostasy bears fruit in the demiurgical presumption of *magic,* a form of animism in which man seeks an authority of the self, placing himself above the law of the universe by attempting to separate the inseparable. He thus creates an unreal world of false contexts after having destroyed or deserted the real. And in this way the method of analysis, of scientific objectivity, which is good and necessary in its right place, is endowed with a destructive power when it is allowed to usurp a place for which it is not fitted.

The naturalist principle that man is the measure of all things has been shattered more than ever in our own age by the question, "What is the measure of man?" Post-modern man is more profoundly perplexed about the nature of man than his ancestors were. He is on the verge of spiritual and moral insanity. He does not know who he is. And having lost the sense of who and what he is, he fails to grasp the meaning of his fellow man, of his vocation and of the nature and purpose of knowledge itself. For what is not understood cannot be known. And it is this cognitive faculty which is frequently abrogated by the "scientific" theory of knowledge, a theory that refuses to recognize the existence of comprehensive entities as distinct from their particulars. The central act of knowing is indeed that form of comprehension which is never absent from any process of knowing and is finally its ultimate sanction.

Science itself acknowledges as real a host of entities that cannot be described completely in materialistic or mechanistic terms, and it is this transcendence out of the domain of science into a region from which science itself can be appraised that *The Credo Series* hopes to expose. For the essence of the ebb and flow of experience, of sensations, the richness of the immediacy of directly apprehended knowledge, the metaphysical substance of what assails our being, is the very act itself of sensation and affection and therefore must escape the net of rational analysis, yet is intimately related to every cognitive act. It is this increasing intellectual climate that is calling into birth once more the compelling Socratic questions, "What is the purpose of life, the meaning of work?" "What is man?" Plato himself could give us only an indirect answer: "Man is declared to be that creature who is constantly in search of himself, a creature who at every moment of his existence must examine and scrutinize the conditions of his existence. He is a being in search of meaning."

Theory and life always go together. An organic conception of man and his work, man and society, man and the universe, is portrayed in First Corinthians 12 when Paul relates the famous story of the strife that once broke out between the parts of the human body. They refused to fulfill their special functions within the organism until they finally learned that they are all parts of one body and can exist and function only as such. For they all breathe together. And by so doing subordinate themselves to the presentation of the whole body. What may be an explanation of organic life in the human body may be transferred to the life in the universe and to the relationship between the interior and the exterior, for all is permeated by the life-giving creative power—by unity.

The authors in this endeavor are aware that man in the twentieth century finds himself in the greatest revolution since the discovery of agriculture. They show, each in his own way, that part of the meaning of our present turmoil may indeed lie in its being the means to reconcile thought and action, to overcome the parochialism of dogmas that only isolate man from man and man from the implicit meaning of his chosen profession. Our effort is to create an image of man intelligible and unitary, a microcosmic mirror of the greater macrocosm of which he is a part and in which he has his legitimate place in relation to the whole. For even the extraordinary successes of scientific predictions, the fruits of man's ingenuity in inventing the scientific method, seem comprehensible only on the basis that the human mind possesses an inherent logic closely parallel with the structure of the external world itself.

The very interdependence of the observer and the participant can no longer be ignored as part of the essential value of things. To take a definitive example from modern cosmology, it is challenging indeed to note that there is a most unusual connection between the existence of stars and the laws that govern the atomic nuclei. Emphasis is placed upon the existence, not the properties, of stars. For everyone expects the properties of stars and atomic nuclei to be related. It is the *connection* with the *existence* of stars that is so reassuring—and indeed surprising.

From this it is evident that there is present in the universe a *law* applicable to all nature including man and his work. Life itself then is seen to be a creative process elaborating and maintaining *order* out of the randomness of matter, endlessly generating new and unexpected structures and properties by building up associations that qualitatively transcend their constituent parts. This is not to diminish the importance of "scientific objectivity." It is, however, to say that the mind possesses a quality that cannot be isolated or known exclusively in the sense of objective knowledge. For it consists in that elusive humanity in us, our self, that knows. It is that inarticulate awareness that includes and *comprehends* all we know. It consists in the irreducible active voice of man and is recognized only in other things, only when the circle of consciousness closes around its universe of events.

The experience of the modern mind has been expressed in terms of conflict produced by false dualisms, disruption, self-destruction, meaninglessness, purposelessness and desperation. This character of our time has found its expression in literature, in art, in existential philosophy, in some forms of natural science, in political demonologies, and is explored in the psychology of the unconscious. Our authors hope to indicate that through a quickening of awareness man can overcome this dualism and can rise to face the meaning of life and work, keeping his mind and energies awake at full stretch. Such knowledge—that form of knowledge which cannot be disjoined from being—will enable man to embrace life with passion and to work with devotion. It will enable him to absorb experience with his whole nature and thereby to fill a want that is satisfied neither by action alone nor by thought alone. This unity of *being* and *doing* has a justifiable claim to be called a form of enchantment since through it men, who might otherwise give in to the malice of circumstances and conditions, find their old powers revived or new powers stirring within them, and through these life is sustained, renewed and fulfilled.

Man is now confronting himself with the compelling need to create an organic identification between what he *is* and what he *does*. For only in this way can the threat of conformism and the treachery of abstraction, the plight of the modern mind, be conquered. This split, inherited from the seventeenth century, between the transitive and the intransitive, between the creator and the process of creativity, has blunted man's appetite for experience. Language itself in our time has failed because man has forgotten that it is the mother of thought, because of its analytical emphasis, and thus lacks ready means to convey associations, emotional or imaginative, that cluster around a subject and give to it a distinctive personal significance. In other words, the symbols by which man lives and has his being, that "tacit coefficient" * of articulate knowledge that is unanalyzable, now knocks at the portals of consciousness waiting to be admitted. For human nature loses its most precious quality when it is robbed of its sense of things beyond, unexplored and yet insistent.

The Credo Series belongs to those ideas that are intuitively conceived and that originate in spheres of a spiritual order and surprise thought, as it were, com-

* See the classical work, *Personal Knowledge,* by Michael Polanyi for an enlarged meaning of the nature of reality. (Chicago University Press, 1958)

pelling it to transform its inherited notions conformably with its enlarged vision of the nature of things. It is as though the authors of the Series were recovering this reality out of a memory of a lost harmony, a memory latent in the soul and not distilled from the changing things of mere physical observation. In this way the inner unity of the known and the knower may be preserved, and the almost mythic intuition of reality thereby related to its conceptual and rational forms of expression. For man, unlike a machine, is an organism existing as an end in itself. He *is* the system on which causal explanations are based and to which they have to return; he *is* a historically existent whole, a four-dimensional entity, and not merely an abstraction from which statements about phenomena are deducible under the guise of eternity.

Our hope is to point to a new dimension of morality —not that of constraint and prohibition but a morality that lies as a fountainhead within the human soul, a morality of aspiration to spiritual experience. It suggests that necessity is laid upon us to infer entities that are not observed and are not observable. For an unseen universe is necessary to explain the seen. The flux is seen, but to account for its structure and its nature we infer particles of various kinds to serve as the vertices of the changing patterns, placing less emphasis on the isolated units and more on the structure and nature of relations. The process of knowing involves an immaterial becoming, an immaterial identification, and finally, knowledge itself is seen to be a dependent variable of immateriality. And somewhere along this spiritual pilgrimage man's pure observation is relinquished and gives way to the deeper experience of awe, for there can be no explanation of a phenomenon by searching for its origin but only by discerning its immanent law—this quality of transcendence that abides even in matter itself.

The present situation in the world and the vast accretion of knowledge have produced a serious anxiety, which may be overcome by re-evaluating the character, kinship, logic and operation of man in relation to his work. For work implies goals and intimately affects the person performing the work. Therefore the correlation and relatedness of ideas, facts and values that are in perpetual interplay could emerge from these volumes as they point to the inner synthesis and organic unity of man and his labors. For though no labor alone can enrich the person, no enrichment can be achieved without absorbing and intense labor. We then experience a unity of faith, labor and grace which prepares the mind for receiving a truth from sources over which it has no control. This is especially true since the great challenge of our age arises out of man's inventions in relation to his life.

Thus *The Credo Series* seeks to encourage the perfection not only of man's works but also and above all the fulfillment of himself as a person. And so we now are summoned to consider not only man in the process of development as a human subject but also his influence on the object of his investigation and creation. Observation alone is interference. The naïve view that we can observe any system and predict its behavior without altering it by the very act of observation was an unjustified extrapolation from Newton's *Celestial Mechanics*. We can observe the moon or even a satellite and predict its behavior without appreciably interfering with it, but we cannot do this with an amoeba, far less with a man and still less with a society of men. It is the heart of the question of the nature of work itself. If we regard our labors as a process of shaping or forming, then the fruits of our labors play the part of a mold by which we ourselves are shaped. And this means, in the preservation of the identity of the knower and the known, that cognition and generation, that is, creation, though in different spheres, are nevertheless alike.

It is hoped that the influence of such a Series may help to overcome the serious bifurcation of function and meaning and may show that the extraordinary crisis through which the world is passing can be fruitfully met by recognizing that knowledge has not been completely dehumanized and has not totally degenerated into a mere notebook over-crowded with formulas that few are able to understand or apply.

For mankind is now engaged in composing a new theme. Life refuses to be embalmed alive. Life cannot abjure life; nothing that lives is born out of nothingness. But nothing, either, can preserve its form against the ceaseless flux of being. Life never manifests itself in negative terms. And our hope lies in drawing from every category of work a conviction that non-material values can be discovered in positive, affirmative, visible things. The estrangement between the temporal and non-temporal man is coming to an end, community is inviting communion and a vision of the human condition more worthy of man is engendered, connecting ever more closely the creative mind with the currents of spiritual energy which breaks for us the bonds of habit and keeps us in touch with the permanence of being in all its plenitude through our work.

And as, long ago, the Bearers of Bread were succeeded by the Bearers of Torches, so now, in the immediacies of life, it is the image of man and his vocation that can rekindle the high passion of humanity in its quest for light. Refusing to divorce work from life or love from knowledge, it is action, it is passion that enhances our being.

We live in an expanding universe and also in the moral infinite of that other universe, the universe of man. And along the whole stretched arc of this universe we may see that extreme limit of complicity where reality seems to shape itself within the work man has chosen for his realization. Work then becomes not only a way of knowledge, it becomes even more a way of life—of life in its totality. For the last end of every maker is himself.

"And the places that have been desolate for ages shall be built in thee: thou shalt raise up the foundations of generation and generation; and thou shalt be called the repairer of the fences, turning the paths into rest." *

—RUTH NANDA ANSHEN

* Isaiah, 58:12

TWO MODES OF THOUGHT:

My Encounters with Science and Education

MY CREDO

As a volume in *The Credo Series,* this book might be expected to deal with the set of beliefs which have guided my actions during the fifty years since I was graduated from college. As a matter of fact I have found it impossible even to start on such an undertaking for two reasons. In the first place, there have been too many sharp discontinuities. For nearly twenty years I was concerned primarily with chemical research and incidentally with Harvard and education. In the next twenty years, I was concerned with Harvard and educational administration (with a brief interlude of administrative work in Washington during the war, which brought me back into contact with scientific work). The last ten years I have devoted all my time and energy, first to the relation between the United States and Germany, and then to a completely different task, the study of American public education.

It is true that all through these years, four themes were entangled—chemistry, Harvard, Germany and education. But I am completely unable to answer such questions as the following: Why did I leave chemistry for educational administration? Why did I retire from the presidency of Harvard at the age of sixty in order to become High Commissioner in Germany? Or why, after four years in Germany, did I choose to make a study of the American comprehensive high schools? Frankly, I am always skeptical of writers who attempt to answer such personal questions. The answers provided seem to be rationalizations after the event. They may or may not provide entertaining reading, but in the light of modern psychology they can only be regarded as a form of fiction. Evidence of this fact is my recollection of the changing ways I have viewed my decision to accept the presidency of Harvard in 1933. The explanation I then had in mind was not the same as I would have offered, say, in 1953, and today I would describe my motives in still a different fashion.

I might attempt to reconstruct the guiding principles in each of my four careers—chemist, college president, diplomat, self-appointed investigator of public education. But my doubt as to the validity of any such reconstruction is the second reason which prohibits the enterprise at the start. In place of it, I shall present, as my intellectual credo, a personal analysis of the way it seems to me people tend to formulate their ideas. This analysis has been slowly developing in my mind over the course of many years. It rests on my interpretation of the history of the experimental sciences (about which I have written from time to time) and the relation of this interpretation to the growth of the social sciences as well as the education of businessmen and lawyers. It has been my experiences in Germany in the 1950's, however, which have brought to a focus a string of impressions which may have had their origin in the eight months I spent in 1925 visiting the laboratories of many German universities. While I was then a chemist talking to other chemists, the differences between the organization of instruction and research in American and German universities made a profound impression on me and to a degree influenced my attitude later as President of Harvard. However, important as these differences are for understanding the intellectual presuppositions of the two countries, they are peripheral to the thesis I am presenting in this volume. And this thesis is the result of years of accumulated experience with professors, teachers, scientists, governmental officials and businessmen in Germany and the United States.

Toward the end of my four-year tour of duty in Germany I presented to an audience at Hamburg University the outline of my analysis of the way people tend to think about human problems. The title of the lecture was "Two Manners of Thinking." I thus completed my formulation of an answer to a set of problems which had begun to plague me in the first years of my duties as a university administrator. My discussions with German officials, professors and businessmen seemed to me to yield the key to a puzzle which I had first encountered in the early 1930's, when I left the laboratory to become a university administrator. Those were the days of the deep Depression. Orthodox and unorthodox social, political and economic theories were being discussed not in abstract terms but with concrete proposals for immediate action as the issues before the social scientists for debate. As the presiding officer of the faculties of law and business administration, as well as arts and sciences, I became increasingly aware of a difference in outlook among the social sciences. To some degree it seemed to be an opposition between the practical and the theoretical outlook, but this distinction was argued in quite different terms from those I was accustomed to hearing among chemists and chemical engineers. A debate on the relative importance of pure and applied science was an old story. But here I was listening to a different sort of disagreement. I was puzzled by the arguments and counterarguments which somehow or other never seemed to meet. Such was my first encounter with the basic question I was later to meet again and again: Is social science a science comparable to the natural sciences?

My first glimpse of a solution of the puzzle was provided by a legal friend, who referred me to a lecture which Lord MacMillan had delivered in Cambridge University in the 1920's, entitled "Two Ways of Thinking." Lord MacMillan had practiced law in both England and Scotland. He was thus able to contrast the legal traditions of the two countries, one of which was the home of the common or case law, while the other was bound to the traditions of the Continental or code law. The differences in the two legal systems Lord MacMillan related to two ways of looking at human problems, which he characterized as the empirical and the deductive. Here was perhaps a clue to some of the differences of opinion I had been hearing, a clue which began to have real meaning only as a result of my experiences as United States High Commissioner in Germany in 1953 to 1955. Expanding and altering somewhat Lord MacMillan's formulations, I arrived at a distinction between "empirical-inductive" and "theoretical-deductive" modes of thought. These were the two modes of thought presented in my Hamburg lecture, the first being characteristic of Americans, the second of Germans—or so I claimed.

More than one German who listened to my lecture agreed with my analysis—granting of course that one is always oversimplifying a situation when one generalizes about national characteristics. I would have been on safer ground, perhaps, if I had directed attention more to the differences in the structure of the educational systems in the two countries and to the basic contrast between the concepts of a university. I was well aware of the contrast because one of my early efforts as High Commissioner had been to promote the idea of the establishment of a business school on the Harvard model in Berlin. The discussion which ensued brought to light the fact that the Americans were thinking about the education of future businessmen in a *university* in different terms from the Germans.

During the last six years I have been primarily concerned with elementary and secondary education in the United States and the education of teachers. Short visits to Switzerland, Italy, France, England, Japan and Germany in this period kept me aware, however, of the fundamental differences between the educational systems of different countries. My analysis of the social sciences seemed to serve me well. I found it particularly useful when I returned to Berlin in June, 1963, for a year's residence as educational adviser to the city (supported by the Ford Foundation). Free Germany in the last few years has been undertaking a soul-searching inquiry into education at all levels. Some of the issues are reminiscent of those I found in the United States recently in my study of the education of teachers. In both countries the question of whether or not there is or can be a science of education is much to the fore at the present moment; this question is closely related to the one that first puzzled me in the 1930's, namely, are the ways of thinking about problems in the natural sciences also applicable in the fields of the social sciences?

What goes on in schools, colleges and universities may be classified as applied social science, or a practical art on which the social sciences are now impinging. At all events, I feel that the time I spent studying education has been in itself an encounter with the theory and practice of one phase of social science. To the extent that the art of teaching school has a scientific basis, one is dealing with the social sciences when one examines the education of teachers. For example, one must consider carefully the nature of those statements about schools which include the word "ought." For such statements may either imply the acceptance of a moral premise or they may imply the acceptance of the conclusion of educational psychologists about such matters as the learning process. In my analysis of the role of the educational sciences (psychology, sociology and anthropology) as contrasted with the role of history and philosophy in teacher education, I have found it useful to look for the contrast between the empirical-inductive and the theoretical-deductive modes of thought. And again the most striking contrast is to be found by talking to applied social scientists (in this case educators) on the two sides of the Atlantic.

I postpone until the concluding chapter a further consideration of educational issues. But I must anticipate my final conclusion, for such a conclusion is essentially what has become my educational credo. I venture to formulate it as follows:

A free society requires today among its teachers, professors and practitioners two types of individuals: the one prefers the empirical-inductive method of inquiry; the other the theoretical-deductive outlook. Both modes of thought have their dangers; both have their advantages. In any given profession, in any single institution, in any particular country, the one mode may be underdeveloped or overdeveloped; if so, the balance will need redressing. Above all, the continuation of intellectual freedom requires a tolerance of the activities of the proponents of the one mode by the other.

The three chapters which comprise this volume are devoted to explaining what is meant by the statements in my credo. Though the aim will be to show the relevance of my classification for those concerned with education and research in the social sciences, I must start with a consideration of the natural sciences and technology. And since the contrast which is basic to my thesis has been largely a contrast between the United States and Europe, I shall have to intrude a consideration of the special history of science and invention in

America in the nineteenth century. I shall also have to contrast the education of lawyers to illustrate the status of the social sciences on the two sides of the Atlantic. Whether in the end the reader finds my analysis satisfactory or not, I hope it may at least illustrate the difficulties encountered when one seeks to discover whether or not the study of man and his work may be regarded as truly scientific. It is with such hopes in mind I have written this volume for *The Credo Series* and present it to the public. For it shows, I trust, the multiple influences which have affected my own thinking and my own attitudes; my own decisions and my own philosophy of life.

I

INDUCTION AND DEDUCTION IN SCIENCE AND TECHNOLOGY

ONE MAY speak of induction as the process of going from particulars to the general and deduction as the reverse procedure. We all think both inductively and deductively in carrying out our daily tasks. We could not operate at all without assuming the validity of many, many generalizations. From these generalizations we deduce specific consequences which guide our immediate conduct. When things turn out differently from our expectations, we usually blame either the generalization which we accepted as a premise or realize that there was a flaw in our deductive reasoning.

At school we learned that geometrical reasoning was deductive. We followed at least a few chains of deductive thought which led to infallible conclusions provided the premises were granted. We may have been led to believe that the method of science in contrast to mathematics was an inductive method. For this was a popular belief a generation or more ago. Indeed, one still hears echoes of it today in some accounts of the so-called scientific method, though the historians and philosophers of science have made it quite clear that there is no one method by which science has advanced.

In terms of the two modes of thought which I mentioned in the Introduction, one can safely say that the natural sciences as they stand today are the result of the careful use of the empirical-inductive method of inquiry together with the imaginative use of the theoretical-deductive. In the last one hundred years in all branches of the natural sciences, the advances have been a consequence of the collaboration of scientists with two different outlooks. Therefore, if we wish to examine the work of those who are emphasizing only the one method, we must turn elsewhere than to the history of astronomy, physics, chemistry or biology. The best place to look, perhaps, is in the shops of those artisans who over the centuries were improving such practical arts as metalmaking and glassmaking; or on the farms where by slow steps agriculture progressed; or in the homes where practical wisdom became embodied in the recipes of the housewives.

Consider any one of the ancient arts which started developing in the dawn of history. We know very little of the way early progress was achieved, since the artisans have left no records of their many trials of new procedures. We can only surmise on the basis of recorded improvements. We know far more about the way progress has been made in more recent times in certain of the arts even before they were transformed by the introduction of scientific concepts. The making of iron and steel is a good example, for it is fair to say that until the advent of the "new chemistry" of Lavoisier in the late eighteenth century, the metalmakers were operating without benefit of science. Sometime in the remote past, men had learned that certain kinds of rocks or dirts when heated with charcoal produced a malleable metal they called iron. The properties of the product depended on the procedure used. Such procedures were the consequence of innumerable trials; oftentimes, perhaps the new idea was the result of an accidental variation in the recipe employed or the materials which were used. The knowledge thus acquired is often called "purely empirical" since there is no admixture of scientific theory. If the practitioner is asked why he proceeds in a certain way, the answer is "because experience has shown this is the best way." The word "experience" covers a multitude of trials—of experiments, if you will—designed to improve the product. Looked at in the light of modern science, we may say the metalmakers before chemistry became a science were experimenting blindly. But they produced results nonetheless. Their successes were triumphs of the empirical-inductive mode of thought.

As a concrete example, consider the revolution in ironmaking in the second half of the eighteenth century in England. Coke from coal was substituted for charcoal from wood. The exploitation of this new process made the "black country" of England the great producer of iron at the end of the century. No longer were the iron masters dependent on the forests; the mining of two materials, coal and iron ore, became the foundations of the industry. Every schoolboy now knows that both charcoal and coke are impure forms of the element carbon; the role of the carbon in ironmaking is primarily to combine with the oxygen of the iron oxide (the ore) to form the gas carbon monoxide and leave the element iron in a molten state. The processes of making either coke from coal or charcoal from wood are essentially the same; in both instances, heating the materials away from air (so they will not burn) drives off volatile material and leaves the nonvolatile element carbon. With this knowledge, it is easy to say why coke can be substituted for charcoal. The explanation is part of elementary chemistry.

The pioneers who started using coke in ironmaking, however, were living just before the chemical revolution of the 1780's. They had no clear ideas of the role of charcoal; they were working *purely empirically* with recipes which had been handed down through the ages. Yet a revolutionary innovation was brought about in this last phase of the purely empirical art of metalmaking. Trial-and-error experimentation without benefit of chemical concepts showed a new way of producing iron. The generalizations on which the new method was based were established, of course, by induction. One assumed that since coal treated in a certain way had proved suitable for the iron furnace, another sample tomorrow would behave in the same manner. A further assumption, that coal from another mine would be just as satisfactory, turned out in some cases to be false. (We now know that if the sulphur content is too high, the iron will be brittle because of some iron sulfide in the metal.) Empirical generalizations are thus *limited* as compared with scientific generalizations; furthermore, the defining ideas (concepts) are usually common-sense terms and lack precision. In short, empirical generalizations are *narrow* generalizations. The reasons for believing in their validity do not go beyond the particular kind of evidence which lead to the generalization.

A Classical Example of Induction

The last point is of prime importance; when I come to discussing the social sciences I shall make much use of the idea of the width of generalizations. Let me, therefore, detain the reader with a rather detailed analysis of a classical example of induction. This is the discovery of what is usually called Boyle's law. In this case we have a clear account of Robert Boyle's experiments on what he called "the spring of the air." In his experiments he measured the volume of air and the pressure acting on the confined air; the records were only roughly quantitative, but they showed that over a considerable range of pressure, the volume was inversely proportional to the pressure. The generalization that the same relation would hold for any other sample of air was repeatedly verified by later experimenters, who pointed out that the temperature must remain constant.

In Boyle's time air was thought of as a homogeneous material; no other gases were known. When, a hundred years and more later, air was shown to be a mixture and many new gases (such as hydrogen) were isolated, Boyle's law was found to apply as a first approximation to them all. That is to say, if one assumed the generalization, one could deduce what the volume would be if one knew the pressure, or vice versa. All such deductions were approximately correct (assuming a constant temperature). Later, when high pressures were employed, it was discovered that the agreement between the deduction from the generalization and the recorded observation became less and less exact as the pressure became greater.

Boyle's Law Becomes a Consequence of a Wide Scientific Generalization

At the time when chemistry was developing rapidly as a science (from 1780 to 1815), Boyle's law was still an empirical generalization. The assumption that it would hold for any new gas could be challenged. The only answer to the challenge was to try a sample and see. Toward the middle of the nineteenth century the situation changed. A relatively narrow empirical generalization became incorporated in the fabric of the kinetic theory of gases. And here we meet for the first time in this book the impact of the theoretical-deductive outlook on an empirical generalization. The significance of such impacts in the history of modern chemistry, physics and biology can hardly be overestimated. Let us see what was involved.

Without attempting to trace the steps by which scientists developed the idea of gaseous molecules, we can say that as a consequence of the writings of both chemists and physicists, a mathematical theory of gases was evolved. On the assumption that a gas was composed of extremely small particles in constant rapid motion, a theoretical picture of a gas could be drawn. In terms of this picture, equations could be deduced in which pressure, volume and temperature (on a special scale) were related as had been found to be the case experimentally at least as an approximation. Thus, a relation identical with Boyle's law could be *deduced* from the theory as a close approximation for *all* gases provided the pressure was not too great. The new generalization—the kinetic theory of gases—was far wider than Boyle's law. A great many different deductions could be made from it, all applicable to a variety of experimental situations. From this point on, if confronted with a new gas, one could say Boyle's law *must* hold as a first approximation or else the whole kinetic theory of gases would have to be given up.

The Broad Generalizations of Science

E. Bright Wilson, Jr., has written, in his *Introduction to Scientific Research:* ". . . physical scientists are prone to rely very heavily on theories before making generalizations and to be extremely suspicious of generalizations . . . if no theories consistent with the rest of their science can be adduced. Purely empirical generalizations are not highly regarded until they have been explained." [1] The explanation to which the author refers is, of course, in terms of a broad gen-

---

[1] E. Bright Wilson, Jr. *An Introduction to Scientific Research*. New York: McGraw-Hill, 1952, p. 160.

eralization—a part of the theoretical fabric of science. A person concerned only with the growth of such a fabric is likely to be not only suspicious but contemptuous of empirical generalizations. He may be but little interested in actual experimentation. He represents, in short, one who is addicted to the theoretical-deductive mode of thought. The mathematical physicist is an example of such a person. He is, however, by no means typical of the chemists or physicists or biologists one meets with every day and certainly not typical of the engineer. Anyone working in a laboratory has to rely in large part on empirical generalizations whether he likes them or not. This is particularly true when it comes to improving technical processes.

A Modern Example of the Empirical-Inductive Approach

Applied science is only in part what the name implies. In chemistry, in electronics, in mechanical engineering, for example, those experimenting to achieve a superior product or process are bound to rely to some extent on empirical rules and recipes. For instance, if a gas is to be used at high pressures and at a temperature not far from the point of liquification, Boyle's law is of little value in predicting the volume at a given pressure, or vice versa. We say colloquially, "Boyle's law doesn't hold under these conditions." Modifications of the law have been developed which are useful for practical purposes. That is to say, the mathematical equation provides a fairly close predictive relationship between volume and pressure under the extreme conditions in question. The modified law, however, contains certain mathematical terms the values of which are chosen so that the "law will hold"! Clearly, such a modified Boyle's law is an *empirical generalization*. Attempts to relate the additional terms to the kinetic theory of gases have not been successful. In short, the development of modified gas laws have been highly useful but it has not advanced the theory of gases.

An example of the empirical-inductive approach to a practical problem is afforded by the story of the invention of the first antiknock gasoline. The time is just after World War I, the place is the research laboratory of an oil company, and the hero is Dr. Midgely, who told me the story shortly after the discovery had been made.

Back in those days, automobiles were running on what are called low-compression engines; the fuel used was straight-cut gasoline. You simply distilled the crude petroleum, took what came off at a certain boiling point, and used it as gasoline. In those days we thought it served very well. But the engineers and the scientists realized that if they could build a high-compression engine, the engine would be far more efficient and the driver of the car would get many more miles per gallon. The only difficulty was that when they built these high-compression engines and fed them with the gasoline then on the market, the engines knocked badly. Indeed, I remember seeing a demonstration engine that knocked so much that it seemed about to knock itself off the stand on which it had been placed.

But there was one fact that gave hope to the research man. There was one hydrocarbon that could be obtained from coal tar—benzene—which, if fed into a high-compression engine, produced no knock. Benzene, however, was far too expensive to be used as a commercial fuel. So the problem that these men were turning over in their minds was this: Is it conceivable that one could put something into ordinary straight-run gasoline to make it behave like benzene in a high-compression engine? In short, is it possible to develop a cheap fuel for a high-compression engine and revolutionize the automotive industry?

One member of the research team conceived the idea that ordinary gasoline might not cause a knock if it were colored red. The idea was a logical deduction from certain theories then current but now discarded. When the idea was suggested to Dr. Midgely, he said, "Let's try it. Go to the storeroom and get some red dye, put it in the gasoline and we'll try it in the engine." But the storeroom-keeper had only water-soluble dyes and pointed out that it would take a week to obtain a red dye which would dissolve in gasoline. With the impatience characteristic of Americans, the research man said, "We can't wait a week. You must have something around this shop that you can dissolve in gasoline that'll make it red. And we'll try it." The shopkeeper replied, "Why don't you try iodine?" Those who are chemists will see the point; they will recall that tincture of iodine is a red-brown alcoholic solution of iodine. So iodine was tried. The straight-run gasoline containing some iodine was fed into the high-compression engine. No knock. Wonderful discovery! But of no practical value; iodine is too expensive. All waited with impatience until the red dye arrived. But when it did and some beautiful red gasoline was used in a high-compression engine, the engine knocked, just the way it had always knocked.

Obviously, there was nothing in the theory after all. There was no point in having red gasoline. But the research men had discovered that there was *one* substance you could put in gasoline which would make it an antiknock gasoline. The next step was to find a cheap substance that could be used. They worked and worked, all to no avail. No other leads, no other ideas. The chief of the laboratory came to Midgely and said, "You've wasted all the money on this project I'm going to put into it. Close it out; the idea is hopeless." But Midgely replied, "I don't think it's hopeless. I just don't believe the universe can be so constructed that there's only one substance—iodine—that will give gasoline this antiknock property. There must be others." "Well," said the boss, "I'll give you a week more. And if in a week you can come up with some other substance, well, then, maybe there's something in your belief."

Faced with a deadline for results, Midgely brought his staff together and directed them to go into the storeroom and, starting with the letter A, to take each chemical in order off the shelf and dissolve it in a sample of the gasoline and feed the gasoline into the engine. This is pure empiricism; this is an example of the trial-and-error way of advancing knowledge. Midgely's hunt soon succeeded. Before they had finished with the A's, they got to aniline, a coal-tar product, and it worked. So, a second substance had been found. The project was continued. As to the rest of the story—as everyone knows, it finally ended up with lead tetraethyl and, in our day, the manufacture of antiknock gasolines.

The story of the discovery or invention of the first antiknock gasoline illustrates both the deductive and the inductive approach to a problem. The deduction from a theory about the relation of absorption of light to the speed of a chemical reaction was erroneous (for several reasons which it is not necessary to go into here). The prediction that if the gasoline was red it would not produce a knock was wrong. Yet the testing of the correctness of this prediction led by a series of accidents and "pure empirical research" to a practical result. In both the advance of the practical arts (or technology) and in science a theory is important to the degree that it is fruitful. Indeed, in my writings about the history and philosophy of sciences I have defined science as "an interconnected series of concepts and conceptual schemes that have developed as a result of experimentation and observation and are fruitful for further experimentation and observation." [2] Such a restricted definition is unsatisfactory to some

---

[2] James Bryant Conant. *Science and Common Sense.* New Haven: Yale University Press, 1951, p. 25.

people, I must admit. They wish to equate science with a quest for the ultimate structure of the universe and would differentiate science from art or poetry by the accumulative nature of scientific knowledge. As Professor T. S. Kuhn has shown in his book, *The Structure of Scientific Revolutions,* the history of science does not afford evidence for such a widely accepted view. Though I think the work of scientists is different from that of artists or poets for several reasons, I agree with Kuhn's conclusion in the final chapter of his brilliant book. He writes: "We are all deeply accustomed to seeing science as the one enterprise that draws constantly nearer to some goal set by nature in advance." He then proceeds to question whether it really helps to imagine that there is some "one full, objective, true account of nature." [3] By implication, at least, Professor Kuhn suggests that it is erroneous to measure scientific achievement by the extent to which we are brought closer to some ultimate goal.

The view that the correct scientific laws and theories are the limiting cases toward which our scientific developments inevitably trend was held by Charles S. Peirce. It represents a more cautious and critical formulation of a popular belief that science was concerned with discovering the real structure of the universe, of solving a puzzle, as it were, to which there is only one answer. My own view is that even the cautious statement of Peirce goes beyond the historical evidence. Scientific revolutions involve such a drastic

---

[3] T. S. Kuhn. *The Structure of Scientific Revolutions.* Chicago: University of Chicago Press, 1962.

reorientation of a scientist's ways of thinking that the idea of a continuous process over long periods of time can hardly be maintained. At any particular time, those concerned with natural phenomena adopt what seems the "simplest conceptual scheme into which the disordered fragments of raw experience can be fitted and arranged," to quote from Professor W. V. O. Quine, who believes that it is "meaningless to inquire into the absolute correctness of a conceptual scheme as a mirror of reality." [4] Certainly in more than one instance in the last two hundred years a scheme believed to be the "mirror of reality" has had to be abandoned. I even question such statements as "This table is *really* composed of empty space in which are electrons and the nuclei of atoms." The little word "really" has emotional overtones and implies that the physicist's picture of a material object is the one and only answer to the question: What is matter? To be sure, from the standpoint of an experimenter concerned with certain materials (but usually *not* wood), it is essential to formulate the structure of matter in some such terms. If the chemist, however, is dealing with the material of which the table is composed, namely, wood, he will talk not in terms of nuclei and electrons but in terms of polymeric sugar molecules. He might maintain the table was really a mixture of large molecules. For the botanist, however, wood is to be thought of in terms of its process of formation. The craftsman skilled in woodworking would think in terms of the material's

[4] Willard Van Orman Quine. *From a Logical Point of View*. Cambridge, Mass.: Harvard University Press, 1953, p. 79.

potentialities for producing aesthetically pleasing objects. To my mind, each of these radically different statements about what a table really is, is just as valid as the others. In short, in making a scientific statement one always has in mind certain terms of reference, certain premises which determine the relevance of what is said.

The point of view about the nature of the natural sciences I have just presented makes it difficult to think of science as a continuous process of refining man's picture of the universe. Yet those who are concerned with advances in the practical arts can hardly avoid speaking in terms of progress. One can scarcely imagine a person who had been a metalmaker two centuries ago refusing to admit, if brought back to life today, that our methods of making metals were superior to his. No such judgments would be likely if the painters or sculptors of the past were given an opportunity for passing on the work of their successors. In other words, the practical arts seem to be an accumulated enterprise in a way the fine arts are not. And for the experimental scientist, with his empirical-inductive orientation, science is usually regarded as an example of accumulative knowledge. Thus, the contrast in the two modes of thought may appear in the unconscious way a scientist regards the history of science.

I turn now to consider again the transition from a practical art to an applied science. Such a transition involves the introduction of concepts or conceptual schemes which were usually developed without regard for their use in improving a practical art. It is convenient, I think, to speak of the introduction of a theoretical component and to characterize the status of a practical art (or technology) by noting the extent of the theoretical component in the generalizations which guide the practitioner. Thus, today the extent of the theoretical component is large in the electronics industry; it is small in winemaking, in brewing and in tanning leather. Advances in the drug industry have been made thanks to the development of the scientific fabric of organic chemistry and to a lesser degree that of physiology; there are still, however, a number of narrow generalizations little connected with any overall theory; many new drugs have been developed on the basis of trial-and-error experimentation. One might say the degree of empiricism in this industry is higher than in brewing but lower than in electronics. Today in almost all industrial activities there is a consistent effort to widen the relevant generalization. What is often involved is the use of instruments developed on the basis of theoretical science, which leads to a more sophisticated type of trial-and-error experimentation than that used a generation or two ago.

Just because the empirical-inductive type of investigation may widen the empirical generalization in a practical art, the idea is sometimes expressed that science itself is a necessary consequence of such labors. Indeed, some popular accounts of what is called "the scientific method" leave the impression that the fabric of science today is the result of the interconnecting of generalizations which have been arrived at by the empirical-inductive type of work. A study of the history of science demonstrates that such a view of the growth of science is false.[5]

The piling up of narrow empirical generalizations does not assure the emergence of generalizations wide enough to serve as scientific theories. Only rarely have new empirical-inductive generalizations played a critical role in the striking advance in science. This fact is of the utmost importance to those who are interested in extending to the study of man the methods of the natural sciences. I shall return to this point in the last chapter. Here I only wish to emphasize that a failure to differentiate between generalizations of different widths has led to a considerable misunderstanding of the way the physical and biological sciences have advanced.

The layman is often confused by the way the words "law," "hypothesis" and "theory" are frequently employed. A law may be an empirical generalization (Boyle's law) or a consequence of a deduction from a wide theory (Boyle's law as a limiting law today). A law may also be hardly more than a premise in a theoretical structure. Perhaps the best example is the assumption introduced into chemistry by Lavoisier, which is best described as the law of the conservation of weight in a chemical reaction. Later this premise became the law of the conservation of mass. The

---

[5] I refer the reader to *The Structure of Scientific Revolutions* by T. S. Kuhn (Chicago: University of Chicago Press, 1962) and to H. Butterfield's *The Origins of Modern Science, 1300–1800* (London: G. Bell and Sons, Ltd., 1949), as well as to the *Harvard Case Histories in Experimental Science.*

nomenclature may change with the times. Thus an important step in the development of the chemists' atomic-molecular theory in the nineteenth century was the introduction of an assumption about gases which for years was known as Avogadro's hypothesis. Later, when the whole theoretical fabric became stronger, the same assumption was called Avogadro's theory. Today, when the atomic-molecular structure of gases is usually presented as a scientific "fact," the numerical consequences of Avogadro's original hypothesis are called Avogadro's number and the statement sometimes is given the name Avogadro's law.

The more one studies the steps by which rapid advances have been made in the natural sciences, the more difficult it is to describe the ways in which wide generalizations and new concepts have originated. The one thing that does seem certain is that one must speak of the *ways,* for there is no single way. This is the reason why it is worse than nonsense to speak of *the* scientific method. I shall attempt to show the diversity by a few examples. For those who are interested in pursuing this subject further, I suggest the reading of some of the books listed in the Bibliography.

For the layman, I think a study of Pasteur's work is most illuminating. Particularly so if one is interested in the scientific study of human behavior, as I am in this volume. For Pasteur's advance of science grew directly out of concern with practical problems. Louis Pasteur's study of fermentation may be said to have provided the conceptual framework for the theory of bacterial disease. Yet he was led to his study of fermentation by his interest in an industrial problem, namely, the difficulties of a distiller in the French city in which Pasteur was a professor of chemistry. His revolutionary paper might seem a matter of small consequence, for it was concerned with the production of a common material—lactic acid. The practical recipes for making lactic acid involved putting sugar and soured milk together and adding chalk from time to time. The evolution of gas in the process makes the mass appear to boil, as is the case in the preparation of alcoholic beverages from sugars; such a process had long been called "fermentation." A living-organism yeast was known to be an essential ingredient of making beer by fermentation, but it was Pasteur who isolated what he called "a new yeast" from the lactic-acid fermentation.

The isolation of a living micro-organism from lactic-acid fermentation was no accident. Quite the contrary. In his first paper announcing his discovery, Pasteur speaks of "certain preconceived ideas" which guided him. The idea—we may call it an hypothesis on a grand scale or a hypothetical broad generalization—was as follows: every substance which in solution is "optically active" has been produced by a process involving a living organism. The phenomena of optical activity need not detain us. Suffice it to say that it is a property of a solution made manifest by passing a beam of polarized light through the solution and examining the orientation of the beam after its emergence from the solution. According to Pasteur's hypothesis, since lactic acid was optically active, there must have been a living organism involved in its formation. He found there was. He further showed that his "new yeast," when introduced into a sugar solution with certain other materials, produced lactic acid. His paper on lactic-acid fermentation opened the whole field of microbiology.

From many points of view it is important to note that Pasteur's hypothesis was different from the kind of working hypotheses we meet in everyday life. We may call our guess as to why our car won't start—the battery is run down—a working hypothesis. Such hypotheses are very limited, of course. Pasteur's hypothesis was one of those which if they become accepted are recognized as *wide* generalizations; they may be called conceptual schemes. They become accepted when the deductions made from them correspond to observations or the results of experiments. We usually say the hypothesis has been confirmed and has become a theory. But such a way of speaking is not an accurate way of stating the situation. For some hypotheses on a grand scale have been accepted for a while and then later discarded because it was too difficult to account for some observations in terms of the theory. The longer a theory has survived and the wider its scope, the more certain we may be that it will continue to survive. Or, better stated, the more certain we are that, if the theory were abandoned, scientists would be faced with a real predicament, the more we can bet that the theory will not be abandoned.

Pasteur's hypothesis we now say is a scientific "fact" or law. In other words, there are no exceptions to it (though it must be more carefully phrased than in my simplified account). What is more interesting even than the bold way Pasteur proceeded on a "preconceived idea" is the way he met the objection of an older, distinguished chemist. At the time Pasteur entered the field, the views of the older chemist (Liebig) were accepted as an explanation of all changes of organic materials commonly called fermentations or putrefactions or decay. Liebig attributed the chemical processes which took place under these circumstances to the presence of complex nitrogen-containing material (such as dead yeast cells). He thought that it was the spontaneous decomposition of such materials that transmitted to other molecules (such as those of sugar) a vibration which transformed the molecules, causing fermentation. Thus, in alcoholic fermentation, the presence of yeast, Liebig said, was necessary because the nitrogenous material in the yeast decomposed and in so doing caused the sugar present to change into alcohol and carbon dioxide. Pasteur's challenge to this idea could be summed up in a sentence: No fermentation without *living* organisms. In support of this view he could show the necessity for *living* yeast cells in alcoholic fermentation, and living micro-organisms in producing lactic acid and a number of other materials.

Not long after his paper on lactic acid, Pasteur wrote as follows: "I found that all fermentations *properly so called,* lactic, butyric, the fermentations of tartaric acid, of malic acid, of urea, were always connected with the presence and multiplication of living organisms. According to my views, albuminous materials [complex nitrogen-containing substances] were never ferments but the food of ferments. True ferments are organized entities"—i.e., living organisms. Note please the words I have placed in italics—"properly so called." Here we see an example of a device used more than once in the history of science. A phrase is employed in order to make a wide generalization hold in spite of a few facts to the contrary. For one must realize that Pasteur had one set of experiments against him from the start. Liebig had shown years before that a water-soluble material present in the skin of the bitter almond had the property of bringing about a chemical reaction in the almond material itself with the formation of an oil. There were no living organisms here (though the almond itself was the product of a living organism). Confronted with this (and a few similar cases), what did Pasteur do—abandon his wide generalization? Not at all; he blandly swept the cases aside by saying they were not "properly so called" fermentations.

Pasteur obviously comes close to arguing in a circle. Nevertheless, his wide generalization (properly protected) carried biochemistry forward for fifty years or more. It can be claimed to be one of the most fruitful hypotheses advanced in the nineteenth century. In the twentieth century, we can extend it still further and in so doing embrace in one conceptual scheme Pasteur's fermentations and also Liebig's exceptions. A vast amount of work, in which both theory and empirical generalizations played a part, has yielded a picture which is probably familiar to most readers. Living micro-organisms during their multiplication do bring about chemical changes in many materials, but they do so because nitrogen-containing substances, which we call enzymes, are a product of the life process; the enzymes are catalysts which can cause the change of certain substances. Liebig had identified such an enzyme (in a highly impure form) in the skin of the bitter almond. For years this appeared as one of the exceptions to Pasteur's rule; no life, no fermentation. Today, who can say whether in the nineteenth century Pasteur or Liebig had been right? In a sense both were; in another sense both were wrong.

Pasteur's work is an example of a theory closely related to experimental work. He started with a bold guess and stubbornly held to it. (He did the same in other investigations, which are also well worthy of careful study.) On the whole, Pasteur's work falls in the category of empirical-inductive research. Yet he was able to formulate wide generalizations, but not of a mathematical nature. The classical examples of the theoretical-deductive approach are to be found in those sciences where mathematical reasoning seems to be inherent in the process of discovering what we call an explanation. Archimedes' proof of the principle which carries his name is an example of the theoretical-deductive mode of thought. A similar example is provided by the writings of Stevin of Bruges in 1600, and those of Pascal half a century later. Pascal, following Stevin, demonstrated the principles of hydrostatics without reference to experimental data. The argument comes down to this: If you accept as a premise the impossibility of perpetual motion, and assume that a liquid has certain properties which real liquids nearly possess (e.g., incompressibility), one can by *deductive* reasoning arrive at a whole series of predictions about the behavior of liquids in connecting vessels. I have called this way of reasoning the geometrical, because it is so similar to the deductive reasoning of Euclid as it used to be presented in school textbooks.

Butterfield in his *Origins of Modern Science* has well said: "If we are seeking to understand this birth of modern science we must not imagine that everything is explained by the resort to an experimental mode of procedure, or even that experiments were any great novelty."[6] Galileo's great advances in physics were largely a consequence of his use of geometrical reasoning. Butterfield and others have shown how often in his writings Galileo refers to what at first might seem to be experiments in the sense in which we use the word. However, a close examination of what he wrote shows that what he had in mind were what Butterfield calls "thought experiments," not real experiments. The same kind of statements occur in Pascal's writings and were ridiculed by Boyle, who was temperamentally in the empirical-inductive tradition. It seems clear that the great strides forward which were made in the seventeenth and eighteenth centuries in physics and chemistry were a consequence of the

[6] H. Butterfield. *The Origins of Modern Science, 1300–1800*. London: G. Bell and Sons, Ltd., 1949, p. 68.

merging of two traditions. The one derives from Euclid and Archimedes and was carried forward by Stevin and Pascal. The other comes from the generations of unnamed artisans who advanced the practical arts by trial-and-error experimentation. In Galileo's work we see reflections of both traditions, as we do also in Newton's writings and those of the founders of the new chemistry in the late eighteenth century. How matters stood in the nineteenth century, I shall consider in the next chapter. But I must detain the reader a few pages further to consider the use of hypotheses on the grand scale in biology.

Recent biographies of two Harvard professors, Louis Agassiz [7] and the botanist Asa Gray,[8] are of particular interest to one exploring the role of working hypotheses of large dimensions in the classic period of the growth of biology as a science. The attitudes of these two men to the publication of Charles Darwin's *The Origin of Species* show how difficult it is for an investigator to drop a hypothesis which has been the guiding principle of his life. Gray was a careful worker with an empirical-inductive turn of mind. His extension of the biologist's knowledge of the genera and species of plants and their geographic distribution places him among the great naturalists of the second quarter of the nineteenth century. Unlike his

---

[7] Edward Lurie. *Louis Agassiz: A Life in Science*. Chicago: University of Chicago Press, 1960.

[8] A. Hunter Dupree. *Asa Gray, 1810–1888*. Cambridge, Mass.: Belknap Press of Harvard University Press, 1959.

contemporary Agassiz, however, he was not committed to a wide hypothesis about the history of the earth. Therefore, he could weigh the evidence presented by Darwin and easily come to the conclusion that the evidence strongly favored the idea of the evolution of species through a process of natural selection.

Agassiz, early in life, long before he came from Switzerland to the United States, had come to a conclusion about the history of the earth. This conclusion he held to as a matter of faith and indeed it was nearly an article of religious faith, as the theory itself had strong theological overtones. One of the essential elements of this view of the geological history of the earth was the idea of successive catastrophes which swept the slate clean, so to speak. Special creations occurred repeatedly in the past and according to a certain pattern. Such a theory was in direct contradiction to one of the assumptions Darwin made, namely, a long continuous history of living things. Darwin may well have had Agassiz in mind when he wrote in the concluding pages of his *Origin of Species* as follows:

> Authors of the highest eminence seem to be fully satisfied with the view that each species has been independently created. To my mind, it accords better with what we know of the laws impressed on matter by the Creator, that the production and extinction of the past and present inhabitants of the world should have been due to secondary causes, like those determining the birth and death of the individual. When I view all beings not as special creations, but as the

> lineal descendants of some few beings which lived long before the first bed of the Cambrian system was deposited, they seem to me to become ennobled.[9]

Here Darwin is appealing to something more than observation of the scientist, something more than the mass of factual evidence brought together so impressively in the fifteen chapters of his book. One can hardly say he is asking the reader to accept his ideas because they "ennoble" nature, yet this word and the two concluding sentences of the book show how elements other than the appeal to "empirical evidence" have played some role in shaping the views of scientists. The last two sentences of *The Origin of Species* are as follows:

> Thus, from the war of nature, from famine and death, the most exalted object which we are capable of conceiving, namely, the production of the higher animals, directly follows. There is grandeur in this view of life, with its several powers, having been originally breathed by the Creator into a few forms or into one; and that, whilst this planet has gone cycling on according to the fixed law of gravity, from so simple a beginning endless forms most beautiful and most wonderful have been, and are being evolved.

The point I wish to make in placing Agassiz' world view in apposition to Darwin's is to show that something other than appeals to factual evidence was in

---

[9] Charles Darwin. *The Origin of Species.* New York: New American Library, 1958.

the minds of both great naturalists; and what is most important, that Agassiz' world view, though soon to be discarded by all geologists and naturalists, proved a *fruitful* working hypothesis on a grand scale during most of Agassiz' lifetime. Like Pasteur's "preconceived ideas," the basis was *not* an inductive generalization. Unlike Pasteur's hypothesis (which in contrast was on a very limited scale), it never attained to the status of a wide generalization, or an accepted conceptual scheme. Why? Because the deductions made from the generalization were often so clearly contrary to the observations. To save the theory, Agassiz or his disciples would have had to add assumption upon assumption. Indeed, before he died Agassiz himself, while never accepting Darwin's views, gave up the attempt to reconcile his own views with the evidence Darwin and his followers were presenting.

In his Introduction to the 1958 edition of *The Origin of Species,* the British biologist Sir Julian Huxley traces the history of Darwin's views. As he states, there was a period of about thirty years at the turn of the century when much of what Darwin had written was subject to heavy criticism by the biologists of the day. By the middle of the century, however, according to Huxley, the developing science of genetics has shown how some of the apparent difficulties of Darwin's postulates about natural selection may be resolved. He states: "Today, a century after the publication of the *Origin,* Darwin's great discovery, the universal principle of natural selection, is firmly and finally established as the sole agency of major evolutionary changes."[10] I have no reason to doubt that Sir Julian is speaking for the vast majority of active biologists in the 1960's, though one can question his (or anyone else's) assurance about the future of a scientific theory or a "universal principle." Therefore, whatever evidence we have as to the origin of Darwin's revolutionary hypothesis is of special interest.

It might seem that here was a case where the empirical-inductive approach had eventually led to the emergence of a new conceptual scheme. Indeed, I remember a generation ago hearing a leading social scientist cite Darwin's work as an example of how the accumulation of "empirical facts" could lead to wide generalizations. Yet a careful examination shows that such an interpretation is not correct. Darwin, to be sure, started by making many observations on a surveying expedition aboard the "Beagle." He was particularly struck by the way in which closely allied species appeared and replaced one another in South America; the near relationship between species inhabiting the islands off the coast and those native to the continent; and the close relationship between the surviving and the extinct species of certain mammals and rodents.

"As I pondered these facts and compared them with

---

[10] It has been pointed out that Darwin, looking back at the origin of his ideas, laid great stress on the fact that he had read Malthus' "Essay on Population" at just the right time. He is quoted as saying that he could not understand how each species could fit its environment so well. He had thought over a vast amount of data, but only after reading Malthus did the idea of natural selection suddenly arise in his mind.

some similar phenomena," Darwin wrote, "it seemed to me probable that closely related species might spring from a common ancestral stock. But for some years I could not understand how each form could be so admirably adapted to its environment. Thereupon I began to study systematically the domestic animals and cultivated plants, and perceived clearly after a time that the most important modifying force lay in man's power of selection and in his use of selected individuals for breeding. When, by a fortunate chance, I then read Malthus' *Essay on Population,* the idea of natural selection suddenly rose to my mind."

The important words of Darwin are "the idea of natural selection suddenly rose to my mind." Such are the flashes of genius that result in a great scientist's conviction that a working hypothesis is far more than an hypothesis—that it is a principle, that it is correct. Unless he is armed with such a conviction, he will not proceed with the laborious testing of the deductions from the generalization; he will not adhere to his hypothesis even when some of the facts are against him. Often it happens in the history of science that the inventor of the wide generalization (which must at the start be an hypothesis) is not the man who explores the consequences in the laboratory or in the field. In terms of the dichotomy of this chapter, those with a preference for the theoretical-deductive mode of thought are the constructors of the theories. The classifiers, the observers, the experimenters are in the empirical-inductive tradition. Yet the examples I have given in these last pages show that the two categories are not necessarily mutually exclusive. The greatest scientists can and have used both modes of thought; the empirical-inductive is by itself insufficient to generate advances in scientific theory. On the other hand, the theoretical-deductive mode by itself is too often barren; for advances in the practical arts it has been in the past quite unnecessary. Indeed, in the next chapter I shall discuss the work of the nineteenth-century inventors and show how discoveries have been made with the minimum of theory even in the age of science.

II

AMERICAN INVENTORS IN THE NINETEENTH CENTURY

IN THE Introduction to this volume I referred briefly to the difference in the prevailing attitudes of the social scientists in American and European universities. Such a difference reflects the preference of Americans for the empirical-inductive approach to human problems. At least, this is one of the theses of my exposition. Anyone familiar with higher education on the two sides of the Atlantic would probably be willing to concede that Americans have the reputation of being empirically minded. For the purpose of this chapter I ask the reader to accept such judgment as a fact and then address himself to the question: How did this come about? My answer, which is far from being an orthodox interpretation of United States history, can be summarized as follows.

In the nineteenth century an essentially agrarian nation was feeling the impact of the industrial revolution and a flood of immigrants; new tools were at a premium; new machines were wanted; the lone inventor became an American hero; his method, essentially the empirical-inductive approach to nature, became accepted as the method of science; carried over into the study of law and later of business administration, sociology and education, the empirical-inductive mode of thought became a characteristic of American social science in the twentieth century, with wide consequences for American schools and colleges.

The preceding paragraph epitomizes my argument. In it the development of a radically new way of training lawyers will occupy a key position. An American lawyer and educator, Dean Langdell of the Harvard Law School, will be classified as a highly successful inventor. His invention was a pedagogic tool, not a material object, to be sure. Yet it was widely adopted and became as revolutionary in its impact on the United States as, say, the McCormick reaper. As everyone is well aware, no invention is widely adopted unless the time is ripe. Langdell's invention is no exception to this rule; what he proposed fitted the needs of the United States in the second half of the nineteenth century. To show why this was so, I must ask the reader to consider the advances in the practical arts made possible by the work of the inventors.

In the last chapter I referred to the revolutionary discovery that coke from coal could be substituted for charcoal in the preparation of iron from iron ore. This discovery, made in England in the late eighteenth century, quite revolutionized the making of iron and steel. It went hand in hand with the British development of the steam engine. One might say that the second half of the eighteenth century was the period of the steam engine and of iron. The nineteenth century, with which

I am concerned in this chapter, was, on the other hand, the period of the inventor, who took advantage of the emerging knowledge of the new sciences of chemistry, electricity and electromagnetism. It was in this field of endeavor that the Americans in the nineteenth century became world famous. In their two-volume history of the United States,[1] Merle Curti, Richard H. Shryock *et al.* point out that in the latter half of the nineteenth century in Europe, the development of science and the practical arts went hand in hand; but in America, although the discoveries of inventors were of world importance, the advances in science by Americans were few and far between. Indeed, the neglect of theoretical science by nineteenth-century Americans was very striking. Neither business, nor the masses, nor the government displayed much interest in research. Government aid to science was largely limited to useful projects in agriculture and mining. The colleges viewed their professors primarily as teachers rather than as research men. The few who were interested in research received scant encouragement.

Willard Gibbs was, perhaps, the most original American scientist of the nineteenth century. To his name should be added that of Joseph Henry as well as Louis Agassiz and Asa Gray. Toward the end of the century the work of Morley, Michaelson and Rowland attracted world attention. Yet the character of the advancement of knowledge in the United States in the nineteenth

---

[1] Merle Curti, Richard H. Shryock *et al. An American History*. 2 vols. New York: Harper & Bros., 1950.

century was determined by the work of the inventors. Run through the names of the famous people of that period connected with technology and science: Whitney, Fulton, Stevens, Morris, Bell, Edison. Starting with Eli Whitney's invention of the cotton gin in 1793, one can count one hundred years of advancement of practical knowledge by Americans, including the inventions of Thomas A. Edison. Both Whitney and Edison were typical of those extremely practical Americans who made an invention because they saw the urgent need for the invention.

The story of Whitney is a good example. A graduate of Yale College just before the turn of the century, he intended to be a lawyer. To that end he went south to study law and at the same time serve as a tutor in a southern family. His attention was called to the desperate financial situation of those who were growing green seed cotton; he saw the need and proceeded to invent the cotton gin. This machine replaced the expensive hand methods of separating the cotton fibers. To be sure, Whitney as a boy had been very handy with his tools; indeed, one of his neighbors said when he went off to college: "There goes the spoiling of a good carpenter." The fact that he was skillful with tools was important. Yet what was more significant was the fact that when he was confronted with a problem he invented a new instrument in a relatively short time. Whitney later was busy in a factory in New Haven, Connecticut, manufacturing arms for the United States government. Before long he introduced the idea of interchangeable parts, thereby reducing enormously the cost in the manufacture of complicated instruments, in this case complicated instruments of war.

Any account of American inventors must include the steamboat story. Yet it is much too complicated for detailed study. A considerable number of people were involved, not only Americans, of course. The Americans to be named include the Stevenses, father and son; Fitch and Rumsey; and Robert Fulton, whose boat the "Clermont" made a trip in 1807 from New York to Albany. Indeed, Fulton is the man we generally associate with the idea of bringing the steam engine from England and putting it in a boat and making steam navigation possible. It is interesting that de Tocqueville, in his famous book on the United States, which was written a generation later, wrote as follows: "These very Americans who have not discovered one of the general laws of mechanics have introduced into navigation an engine that changes the aspects of the world."

Next we come to a group of inventors concerned with the application of the newly discovered phenomena of electricity and electromagnetism. Samuel F. B. Morse, the portrait painter turned inventor, developed his telegraph and his Morse code and erected the first practical telegraph line from Washington to Baltimore in 1844. We might mention also the laying of the first transatlantic cable by Cyrus Field. Of course, one must remember that Morse received help from Joseph Henry, the scientist who was active in purely scientific research in the new field of electricity.

A generation after Morse comes Alexander Graham Bell, the inventor of the telephone. It is always a question whether we are being fair to call him an American, since he was born and brought up and educated in Scotland and was at first a professor in London. But he did come to the United States in 1873 as a professor of vocal physiology and the mechanics of speech in Boston. It was after his migration to this country that he started to improve Morse's telegraph. It seems clear that in addition to trying to improve the telegraph—and everybody was doing that at the time—he had a very definite idea that what was needed was an instrument that would carry the human voice over a wire. Within three years of his starting to work on the problem, he was able to transmit the first telephone message to his assistant: "Mr. Watson, come here. I want to speak to you."

Finally, toward the end of the century we meet Thomas A. Edison, who in my youth epitomized the American inventor. His most original invention was that of the phonograph in 1877, when he was thirty years of age. Yet his incandescent lamp is probably the most important of his many inventions. Taken together with what he did to develop the art of generating electricity, it made possible a city whose houses were lighted by electricity. The idea of an incandescent lamp was not original with Edison. An Englishman named Swan had already shown that a carbon filament in an evacuated bulb could serve as the basis of an electric lamp. But those researches of Swan's, compared with Edison's, were qualitative. The European and the English lamps worked irrespective of cost, while the costs of Edison's were measured at every point. Edison succeeded first with a filament made from a cotton thread which remained incandescent for forty hours in an exhausted bulb. He is said to have tried thousands of carbon-containing materials from tar to cheese and experimented with six thousand different sorts of vegetable fibers collected from all parts of the world. Bamboo gave the most durable filaments.

Six thousand different sorts of vegetable fibers! Here we see the empirical-inductive mode of thought, an example of trial-and-error experimentation. One works almost blindly in that there is no theory to guide the way. That is, blindly except for the goal, in this case a cheap filament that would last. Indeed, this method of Edison's—the trial-and-error method—has often been spoken of as the "Edisonian method of experimentation," a synonym for what I am calling the empirical-inductive mode of thought.

Edison's early career was that of a young boy struggling through many hardships. When he was twenty-one he had saved enough money to buy a set of writings of Michael Faraday, the great British chemist and physicist of the mid-nineteenth century. Edison's electrical inventions may be said to be a consequence of his reading of Faraday's researches on electromagnetism. To me it is interesting to contrast what Edison did with the knowledge thus acquired with what James Clerk Maxwell did with much the same knowledge. Maxwell (born in 1831) was trained as a mathematician and became the first professor of physics at Cambridge University in England. He is the founder, so to speak, of the theoretical interpretation of Faraday's work. His differential equations are the basis of the electromagnetic theory of light. Edison as a young man would not have known a differential equation if he had seen one. Differential equations were what Maxwell lived on. He constructed a theoretical mathematical framework for a large part of physics. His work is an example, par excellence, of the theoretical-deductive approach to science.

In the nineteenth century, the scientists and inventors had a tendency to look down their noses at each other. This fact is amusingly illustrated by a lecture which Clerk Maxwell gave in 1878 at Cambridge University —a lecture on the telephone. Here is what this famous professor—the exponent, so to speak, of the theoretical-deductive method—had to say about Alexander Graham Bell's discovery:

> When about two years ago news came from the other side of the Atlantic that a method had been invented of transmitting by means of electricity the articulate sounds of the human voice so as to be heard hundreds of miles away from the speaker, those of us who had reason to believe that the report had some foundation in fact began to exercise our imagination, picturing some triumph of constructive skill–something as far surpassing Sir William Thomson's siphon recorder in delicacy and intricacy as that is beyond a common bell pull. When at last this little instrument appeared, consisting, as it does, of parts every one of which is familiar to us and capable of being put together by an

> amateur, the disappointment arising from its humble appearance was only partially relieved on finding that it was really able to talk.

And later in the same lecture Maxwell said, "Now, Professor Graham Bell, the inventor of the telephone, is not an electrician who has found out how to make a tin plate speak, but a speaker who, to gain his private ends, has become an electrician."

Bell's invention was hailed by the scientific community later, so that Maxwell's comment is not typical of the scientists' eventual reaction to Bell's work. But it is representative of a certain gulf in the nineteenth century between those who were practicing two modes of thought. A story connected with Edison illustrates the same point. Edison at the time of America's entering into World War I was appointed by President Wilson as chairman of a committee on science to assist the government. And Edison undertook the task. Somebody suggested he should have a mathematician on his committee. And Edison is alleged to have agreed reluctantly, remarking: "Well, yes, I guess you better add a mathematician. We might have to figure something out."

I have been discussing the relation of science and invention in the nineteenth century, *not* in the mid-twentieth, and I pause to remind the reader of the vast changes which have taken place in technology since 1900. The lone inventor has all but disappeared. The distinction between the empirical-inductive and the theoretical-deductive can be found only in a modern industrial research laboratory by one who is keenly interested in the methods of invention and discovery. Those who relish logical lines of argument from high-level theories and sit at their desks all day may have their private contempts for those who love the machine shop, the laboratory and the pilot plant. But the vast electronic calculators, the enormous advances in the theories of physics as demonstrated by the developments in atomic energy, make it impossible in most areas of technology for those who delight in trial-and-error experimentation to get on without the theoreticians. Such being the case, it can be argued that a knowledge of the history of the nineteenth-century gap between inventors and scientists can only confuse the layman interested in science and technology in the 1960's.

I agree. If my purpose were only to present a picture which would lead to a better understanding of science and invention, I should not have written as I have. But my interest is quite otherwise. I am primarily concerned in this volume not with the natural sciences and their application but with the social sciences. I am trying to throw light on the fact that the social sciences in the United States have developed in a rather special way and in this century developed fast.

There is, of course, no single explanation, but one of the important factors, it seems to me, was the fact that during the second half of the nineteenth century a majority of highly educated Americans came to associate the word "science" with the success of the American inventors. Closely related to this process of association was the focusing of attention on the work of the systematic biologists. This was a period when Newton's synthesis had already been assimilated in the stock of common knowledge. The excitement of the eighteenth century over celestial mechanics had subsided. The vast theoretical structure of the nineteenth-century physics was in the process of construction but in the 1860's had not yet been popularized. The dramatic scientific event was the publication in 1859 of Darwin's *The Origin of Species*. As I have already indicated, the evolution of Darwin's ideas is an example of the blending of the empirical-inductive with the theoretical-deductive. Yet, for the layman, the collection of the evidence which Darwin presented to support his revolutionary theory might be considered as *the* example of the scientific method. Facts had been collected and ordered. A given specimen was placed in an evolving framework of classification. This was not the experimentation of the American inventor, to be sure, yet it was the empirical-inductive approach. This was the mode of operation of the systematic naturalist, which had been proceeding for generations but with an accelerating pace in the second half of the nineteenth century. Louis Agassiz, who was the great scientific figure in Cambridge, Massachusetts, was an example of the supreme naturalist. Although, as I have pointed out, he refused to accept Darwin's views, his mode of thought and that of his Harvard fellow naturalist Asa Gray was in the empirical-inductive tradition.

When Agassiz came to Harvard in the late 1840's, education was about to undergo one of its revolutionary changes. In the next thirty years science was to be taught by observation, not by memorizing textbooks. As late as the first years of President Eliot's regime (the 1870's), laboratory work and observation by students was still a novelty. The new pedagogy was met by skepticism from some of the older generation. The story goes that Eliot was once discussing with enthusiasm the new method of instruction, which involved stimulating the student to make his own observations and draw his own conclusions. "But," expostulated a conservative who was listening with reluctance, "this is no fit procedure for a college; this is the way a puppy learns." "Exactly," replied Mr. Eliot, "and a puppy learns quickly and effectively." I cannot vouch for the authenticity of this anecdote, but it well illustrates the spirit of the educational reformers associated with the introduction of science into the college curriculum.

A highly significant aspect of the impact of the new science on American education after the Civil War was the development of the case method of studying law by the new Dean of the Harvard Law School, Christopher Columbus Langdell. The story has often been told of how Charles William Eliot, who was to become President of Harvard in 1869, came to know Langdell. Eight years younger than this earnest student of the law, Eliot as a senior in Harvard College and later as a tutor in mathematics and chemistry, underwent an experience not uncommon in colleges and universities. He found not only a kindred spirit but also an intellectual hero. Years afterward, the President of Harvard, writing of his talks with Langdell, said: "I was a mere boy, only eighteen years old; but it was given me to understand that I was listening to a man of genius." When, some twenty years later, the student of chemistry was in a position to act on his understanding, he called Langdell to Harvard as Dane Professor of Law, and shortly thereafter made him Dean.

I have not been able to find any clear record of how Langdell came to develop his novel pedagogic doctrines. The best evidence seems to be in what he himself wrote. It is of significance, however, that only a year elapsed after his coming to Harvard before he published his first book, *A Selection of Cases on the Law of Contracts.* In the Preface he set forth those principles some inkling of which must have been perceived by the young Eliot and must surely have been well known before the invitation to join the Harvard Law Faculty was issued. In Langdell's own words, those principles were: "Law, considered as a science, consists of certain principles or doctrines. To have such a mastery of these as to be able to apply them with constant facility and certainty to the ever-tangled skein of human affairs, is what constitutes a true lawyer; and hence to acquire that mastery should be the business of every earnest student of the law." [2]

"Law, considered as a science," wrote Langdell. What did he have in mind when he wrote that word "science"? Not the kind of activity in which at that time Clerk Maxwell was engaged; not the development

---

[2] Christopher Columbus Langdell. *A Selection of Cases on the Law of Contracts: With References and Citations Prepared for Use as a Textbook in Harvard Law School.* Boston: Little, Brown, 1871.

of the atomic-molecular theory, which was then in progress, one aspect of which was that theory of gases referred to in the preceding chapter. Langdell was thinking of science much as was Bell or Edison. His first case book, in which he set forth his new educational ideas, was published in 1871, at the time Edison was developing his incandescent light and only a few years before Bell's invention of the telephone. To me, therefore, Langdell is to be placed among the great American inventors of the nineteenth century. The consequences of his inventions are the subject of the next chapter.

III

THE EDUCATION OF LAWYERS AND BUSINESS EXECUTIVES

At the close of the last chapter, I gave, as an example of the impact of the empirical-inductive mode of thought on education, Langdell's invention of the case method of studying law. I pointed out that in expounding his educational method he specifically referred to law as a science, and by science he clearly meant the reaching of generalizations by careful objective examinations of the records. The analogy with the work of the geologist is apparent from what he wrote in the Preface to his first book, from which I have already quoted. It should be the endeavor of every student of the law, he said, to acquire a mastery of the principles or doctrines of the law. Each of these doctrines, he goes on to say, "has arrived at its present state by slow degrees; in other words, it is a growth, extending in many cases through the centuries." And then comes the proclamation of his new pedagogic principle. "This growth is to be traced in the main," he writes, "through a series of cases; and much the shortest and the best if not the only way of mastering the doctrine effectually is by studying the cases in which it is embodied." [1]

The analogy with geology was made explicit by one of Langdell's early admirers, who introduced the case method into another university school of law. "Under this system," he declared, "the student must look upon the law as a science consisting of a body of principles to be found in the adjudged cases, the cases being to him what the specimen is to the geologist." [2] Another eminent proponent of the case method, Roscoe Pound, preferred to speak in terms of the science of biology and in reviewing the long struggle in getting the method accepted by the bar, said in 1903: "As teachers of science were slow to put the microscope and the scalpel into the hands of students and permit them to study nature, not books, so we have been fearful of putting reports into their hands and permitting them to study the living law." [3]

Fear there must have been among the profession, for a long struggle was involved before the case method attained a position of respectability and before it was adopted by other schools. President Eliot appointed Langdell in 1870 and shortly thereafter gave him a free hand to reform the teaching according to his novel ideas. It was not until 1890, however, that a second law school, the Columbia Law School, adopted the case

---

[1] Quoted by Prof. Joseph Redlich in his "The Case Method in American Law Schools," *Bulletin No. 8* of the Carnegie Foundation for the Advancement of Teaching. New York, 1941, p. 11.

[2] Quoted by Redlich, *loc. cit.*, p. 16.

[3] Quoted by Redlich, *loc. cit.*, p. 16.

method. During those twenty years Langdell and a few disciples, notably Thayer and Ames, had to combat the hostility of the profession; at least one law school was founded in this period for the sole purpose of counteracting the new radical methods of instruction which were developing at Harvard University.

An eminent Austrian professor of law, Professor Redlich, reviewing the rise of the case method from the point of view of an objective observer, has given it as his opinion that: "Langdell's method created an extraordinary radical change, as it were at a single stroke." [4] And he goes on to explain that: "Up to that time the main feature in American law schools had been the memorizing of more or less stereotyped subject-matter, systematically presented in the text book. . . . The new method, on the other hand, proceeds from a fundamentally different conception of the task. . . . To Langdell and his followers the most important means of instruction is the analysis of the separate cases *by* the *student*. . . . Under the old method law is taught to the hearer dogmatically as a compendium of logically correlated principles and norms, imparted ready-made as a unified body of established rules. Under Langdell's method these rules are derived, step by step, by the students themselves by a purely analytical process out of the original material of the common law, out of the cases. . . ." [5] Professor Redlich summed up the matter thus: "The case method is an entirely original creation of the Americans in the realm of law . . . it

---

[4] Redlich, *loc. cit.,* p. 12.
[5] Redlich, *loc. cit.,* p. 13.

is indeed particularly noteworthy that this new creation of instruction in the common law sprang from the thought of a single man, Christopher Columbus Langdell, who, as the originator of this method, became the reformer of the Harvard Law School, and in this way of American university law schools in general." And further on in his report to the Carnegie Foundation, Professor Redlich states: ". . . the case method is, then, in a certain sense, nothing but the return to the principles of legal education demanded by the very nature of the common law." [6] In other words: "the critical analysis of the law case was established as that application of inductive methods which alone was thoroughly suited to the nature of the Anglo-American law." [7]

"The nature of the Anglo-American law": these words of the Austrian professor take me back to Lord MacMillan's concern with the two ways of thinking —one characteristic of the European or code law, the other of the Anglo-Saxon common law. The way Lord MacMillan formulated the difference was as follows:

> . . . the system of Code Law and the system of Case Law, exemplify the two main types of mind, the type that searches for principle and the type that proceeds on precedent. The two methods are the result of widely divergent temperaments. . . . Constitutionally the Englishman has always in practical affairs of life been suspicious often rightly so of the apostle of principle. It was an Englishman (Lord Westbury) who

---

[6] Redlich, *loc. cit.*, p. 37.

[7] Redlich, *loc. cit.*, p. 17.

> wrote "distinctive particularly of the English mind–a love of precedent, of appealing to the authority of past examples rather than to indulge in abstract reasoning." All this is constitutionally repugnant to the continental disciples of the Civil Law. To them the principles of law are what matter. The particular case must be decided not by invoking previous decisions but by logically subsuming it under the appropriate proposition applicable to it.[8]

The professors of law and the practicing lawyers with whom I have discussed Lord MacMillan's thesis are inclined to think that he overstated the contrast he was making. Or else in the forty years since he wrote, the evolution of the practice of law on the continent of Europe has made the distinction far less sharp than it was in former times. To a layman, the striking difference between the two systems of the law is the role played by the decision of judges—the appeal to precedent to which Lord MacMillan refers. It would be an oversimplification to say that in arguing a case an American lawyer depends largely on the authority of previous decisions, while the civil-law lawyer argues on principle; nevertheless, such a generalization seems to reflect the methods of instruction of future lawyers in the United States and Europe. More than one European lawyer has expressed amazement to me at the way the case method is used in American law schools. (And more than one European businessman has expressed

---

[8] Hugh Pattison, Lord MacMillan. "Two Ways of Thinking." Rede Lecture, Cambridge University, 1934, pp. 12–13.

equal amazement at the case method of studying business administration—which I shall discuss shortly.) Langdell was able to develop the case method because the material to be used by the students, the judicial opinions, were right there in a law library ready to be used. And such material, as he well knew, was used every day by the members of his profession in preparing their arguments. Thus, if I am right, it was a combination of the nature of the common law, the American proclivity for empirical-inductive thinking and the educational reforms of the mid-nineteenth century which produced the revolutionary pedagogic device, the case method of studying law.

If the United States in the early nineteenth century had had in existence a well-established system of preparing lawyers, it is unlikely that Langdell's inventive genius would have had a chance to influence pedagogy. On the European continent the law was taught by professors of the law in the spirit characterized by Lord MacMillan by the words "rational and deductive." In England, the Inns of Court had provided a way in which a young man read law among practitioners. In Colonial times and in the first half of the nineteenth century a large fraction of the lawyers in America were inducted into their profession by what was essentially the apprentice system. A young man read law in a lawyer's office—a system not too different from the British. But in the period in which our older colleges were transforming themselves into universities and new universities were being founded, formal instruction in the law, like formal instruction in medicine, was trying to find a place for itself within the embryonic system of higher education. Right after the close of the Civil War, a period of rapid change and expansion (except in the South) began. Thus Langdell was able to incorporate his imaginative ideas in the evolving structure of the academic world in a way which would have been impossible either in Great Britain or on the continent of Europe.

I must add that the evolving system of higher education in the United States from 1870 on assured that more and more men trained as lawyers were educated in university schools of law. And after the 1890's this meant more and more were exposed to the empirical-inductive mode of thought. How this affected the approach of Americans to business and political problems, and in more recent years the approach of scholars to the social sciences, I shall discuss in later pages. Here, I only want to note that the period of the emergence of Langdell's case method as *the* method of studying law was also the period in which Peirce and James and later Dewey were formulating their philosophic views. Whether Langdell ever talked with Peirce or James I do not know. But it is of interest that all three were well-known figures in Cambridge, Massachusetts, when Harvard University was a very small community of scholars. As compared with those of their European contemporaries, the views of all three, I venture to suggest, reflect a preference for the empirical-inductive mode of thought.

Professor Redlich, the Austrian lawyer from whose report I have already quoted, writing in 1913, said:

> . . . the so-called case method is really nothing more than a form of the long existing empirical method of studying and teaching practice law; a form better adapted to modern resources for the study of the common law . . . it was empirical instruction that the young law apprentices since the thirteenth century sought and received in the Inns of Court [in England] . . . The really new thing in Langdell's contribution is the transformation of the old empirical method of teaching into a new empirical method; and the actual ingenious "discovery" that he made in this connection, and which his pupils later perfected, is at bottom only the modern case book . . . in spite of the fact that this purely practical aim has been the ruling purpose . . . Langdell and his followers were none the less justified in describing their method of legal instruction as truly scientific.[9]

And reverting to his earlier discussion of the claim that the case method was inductive, he went on to say:

> Not on the ground that it is an inductive method, but on the ground that it is that method of instruction which is entirely suited to the established character of the common law, to independent intellectual assimilation of positive law from its sources, and to the highest development of the ability to think logically and systematically—on these grounds the case method must indeed be recognized as the scientific method of investigation and instruction in the common law.[10]

In other words, whether the case method be considered as an inductive scientific approach to the law

---

[9] Redlich, *loc. cit.*, pp. 58–59.
[10] Redlich, *loc. cit.*, p. 59.

or an empirical pedagogic device, it had proved its value up to the hilt as a way of training lawyers for practice. So Professor Redlich concluded fifty years ago; and, in spite of much discussion of the pros and cons of the method, it is easy to assemble witnesses today who would testify to the practical value of what Langdell started insofar as the legal profession is concerned.

As evidence of the way Langdell's invention of the case method has affected the thinking of the legal profession, I quote from *The Nature of the Judicial Process,* written by Justice Benjamin N. Cardozo in 1921: "The common law does not work from pre-established truths of universal and inflexible validity to conclusions derived from them deductively. Its method is inductive, and it draws its generalizations from particulars."

And Justice Cardozo quotes with approval from Munroe Smith's *Jurisprudence* (New York: Columbia University Press, 1909): "In their effort to give to the social sense of justice articulate expression in rules and in principles, the method of the lawfinding experts has always been experimental. The rules and principles of case law have never been treated as final truths, but as working hypotheses, continually retested in those great laboratories of the law, the courts of justice." [11]

The reader will note how Justice Cardozo placed deduction and induction in opposition and that both he and Smith speak of the common law as the case

---

[11] Justice Benjamin N. Cardozo. *The Nature of the Judicial Process.* New Haven: Yale University Press, 1921, pp. 21–23.

law. By implication the contrast is made with the code law, in which the reasoning is deductive. Yet, it is evident that in the common law there are rules and principles which are the premises of a chain of deductive reasoning in a given situation. What Langdell introduced was a systematic formal method by which the student discovered these principles for himself, or so it was alleged. The emphasis in such a pedagogic process is on the empirical-inductive, not the theoretical-deductive, mode of thought. And lawyers thus educated carry over into their writings such words as "inductive," "hypotheses," "experimental" and "laboratories"—words characteristic of the natural sciences as those sciences were conceived in the late nineteenth century.

It is beyond my capacity to follow the arguments of the last forty years among lawyers, which seem to turn on the degree of flexibility in the principles of common law. One group of extreme writers, popular a decade or two ago, appeared to consider that the generalizations which should guide a lawyer in advising his client were extremely narrow generalizations. Indeed, they were regarded essentially as predictions about the personal reactions of the judge or judges! Such an attitude is shocking to many laymen and certainly to some lawyers. To Europeans in particular it is almost incomprehensible. Even the arguments that Professor Redlich heard in the United States, fifty years ago, in support of the case method of studying law, he felt were erroneous. The analogy between the inductive discovery of the principles of the common law and the inductive principles of physical science, he felt, was false. (Rarely if ever does one hear such an analogy put forward today, a significant fact.) Redlich stated:

> Legal science cannot deal with law in the sense of the physical investigator, but only with law in the sense of definite norms, willed by men, and intended to guide and limit the business of men. Even in the unwritten customary or judge-made law of England and America, these general norms have long existed, developing widely and in manifold ways. . . . The judge who, in the individual case, decides according to the common law, applies consciously or unconsciously to the state of facts before him, one of these already existing norms or several of these norms in logical connection, and pronounces, as a result of his intellectual process of thought embodied in the judgment, only the rule or norm applicable to the specific case. His intellectual activity in this is, therefore, essentially deductive; for by deduction we mean the application of an already existing rule to the particular case. The fact that these norms of the common law are not codified—does not alter the fact that they exist, and that from the very beginning they dominate all legal life, both the parties who seek the law and the judge who declares it. . . . Out of the entire body of law, published in the form of an enormous mass of prior decisions, he [the judge] finds the norm as it were. The principle, however, that resides in the norm, and that finds expression also in the particular decision, has always existed *a priori,* and its application in the particular case is an instance of logical deduction from that principle . . . the law follows in the end a deductive, not an inductive, path.[12]

---

[12] Redlich, *loc. cit.,* pp. 56–57.

One needs only to read this statement of an eminent lawyer trained in the continental tradition and compare it with Judge Cardozo's views about the law to see the contrast which is the essence of my thesis. Both men were writing about the common law, but one having been educated in the United States and the other in Austria, they came to opposite conclusions. Is the common law an example of inductive or of deductive reasoning? I suggest that the question is just as much an oversimplification as would be the same question about natural science. The laboratory man, like the inventor and the naturalist of the nineteenth century, regards science as primarily inductive; the theoretical physicist looks at modern physics as a triumph of the theoretical-deductive mode of thought. A generation or more ago, when Redlich, Cardozo and Lord MacMillan wrote, the code law was to common law as mathematical physics is today to the empirical development of new drugs. The passage of time, I have been told, has softened the contrast between the two great systems of the law. This may be so; but the methods of introducing the future practitioner to the two systems remains largely unaltered. It is these pedagogic systems, I submit, that fix the preference for the two modes of thought. Graduates of American law schools tend to think in the empirical-inductive mode; those who have listened to lectures in the legal faculties of German or French universities are conditioned to think in theoretical-deductive terms.

If all Americans who studied law continued in their profession and all Germans who were registered as students in a legal faculty became lawyers, the contrast I have just brought out would be far less significant than it is. As a matter of fact, the United States and Germany have one thing in common. Those who complete their formal studies in a university school of law are to be found later in great numbers in important positions in business and in government. Unlike England, studying law became, several generations ago, a sort of final general education for men who had ambitions to be leading men of affairs. In the United States one has only to note how many members of Congress and of the state legislatures were trained as lawyers. In Germany today, as in former times, one finds more often than not that the civil servant (including those in foreign service) studied law in a university. Eighteen of the forty-four members of Chancellor Adenauer's four cabinets (1949–63) studied law in a university. Professor Ralf Dahrendorf of Tübingen has pointed out that these and similar statistics demonstrate that the German universities over the years have been building an elite which consists of those who studied law. And the author goes on to say that the way law is studied by the university student is far removed from being an introduction to practice. Only after passing the first state examination does the future German lawyer leave the university and become familiar with his profession by what may be called a supervised apprenticeship.

Law as a science—more nearly comparable, perhaps, to mathematics than to, say, chemistry—is expounded by the European professors in their lectures. Since many of those who attend have no intention of ever practicing law, the attitude which develops in the student body, according to Dahrendorf, is far from being professional as Americans would use the term. In one sense the German law faculties serve to select and train an elite much as have the English public schools in the past. But the point of view developed is quite different. Dahrendorf, pointing to the more formal tradition of the code law as compared with the common law, believes the university education in law tends toward the development of a sort of authoritarian legalism in German politics and business. With this attitude goes a "widely spread mistrust of common sense." [13] He concludes that for a wider dissemination of fundamental liberal thought, other disciplines than law would be better media for the formation of an elite. If I understand the situation correctly, this is true in German universities just because the code law is presented from the theoretical-deductive standpoint. I should be ready to maintain, however, that because of the empirical-inductive approach to the common law, American law schools do serve in part for the formation of an intellectual elite who do *not* despise common sense and who do *not* think in terms of authoritarian legalism. Quite the contrary, by and large those trained in the case method of studying law have an inquiring attitude, a distrust of wide generalizations, an anti-totalitarian bias.

If all this be true, differences in reactions to many

---

[13] *Der Monat,* July, 1962.

human situations which I have noted among Germans and Americans can be traced in no small measure to the number of former law students in both countries in positions of importance and the fundamental difference in their education. A striking example of the contrast came to my attention more than once in the years I was in Germany. The issue involved the education of future businessmen. The American approach involved the use of the case method of instruction, and I shall never forget a conversation in which a leading economist of a German university denied that such a kind of education had any place in a university. It was far too empirical to suit his taste. And although I should not want to claim that all schools of business in the United States use the case method, I think it is relevant for me to discuss the evolution of this method as another example of the inductive-empirical approach of Americans. It was no accident, of course, that the case method was developed in the Harvard Graduate School of Business Administration by Dean Wallace Donham, who had studied in the Harvard Law School early in this century. In a report on behavioral sciences at Harvard occurs the following passage:

> The case method used at the [Harvard Business] School is based on the principle that one must learn by doing. It is aimed at developing the student's capacity to make sound decisions and to take action by making him act. The student is repeatedly placed in situations where as an administrator he must not only evaluate evidence and opinions but also act with responsibility. . . . The case method of instruction used

> so long at the School has emphasized the practical problems of decision-making in concrete realistic business situations. . . . Since the war, therefore, instruction at the School has stressed the fact that practical business problems involve not only substantive aspects in reaching a decision in the context of the community around us but also the administrative problems of getting a job done. . . . The instruction, almost entirely by the case method, not only utilizes the discipline of economics on which the School was originally based, but has also begun the adaptation to problems of business administration of knowledge, skills and methods of analysis derived from all the behavioral sciences.

Further light is thrown on the content of the cases studied by the students in those business schools in the United States which use the case method by the following statement from the same report:

> Most of the research projects at the Harvard Business School involve field investigation and observation to ascertain what businessmen actually consider and do in dealing with a particular problem. In fact, this type of *empirical* research represents an *inductive* approach wherein the comparison, analysis, interpretation and evaluation of assembled business experience will reveal, if existent, useful generalizations.[14]

These excerpts establish that those who are instructing future businessmen at Harvard, at least, are committed to the empirical-inductive mode of thought. And

---

[14] *Behavioral Sciences at Harvard;* Report by a Faculty Committee. Cambridge, Mass.: Harvard University Press, 1954, p. 346.

it is just this commitment which is challenged by many Europeans. The consequences of such a challenge for the development of universities in the United States and Germany are considered in the next chapter, in which I shall consider generalizations regarding human behavior and conduct. Before embarking on a further exploration of the empirical-inductive and theoretical-deductive modes of thought in the social sciences, however, I must devote a few pages to contrasting the educational system of the United States with that of continental countries insofar as it involves the education of businessmen. For I do not want to leave the reader with the idea that the instruction in the Harvard Graduate School of Business Administration is typical of the kind of education for a business career provided by most institutions. Not all graduate schools of business are as committed to the case method as Harvard. But what is more important, a large proportion of the instruction given in American institutions and labeled "business" or "commerce" is given at the *undergraduate* level. The students in the undergraduate courses are obviously less mature and are usually far less able intellectually than those who are admitted to the highly selective graduate schools of business. The case method could hardly have been developed with students of only average ability who were four years younger than graduate students. Evidences of this approach are therefore hardly to be found in undergraduate schools.

The German who wishes to study in a university must with few exceptions enroll in one of three types of university-preparatory schools at the age of ten or twelve. After a vigorous course of study, during which many drop by the wayside, a set of examinations is taken, and, if these are passed, the student is enabled to enter any university. In terms of the maturity of the student and his competence in languages and mathematics, the young man or woman who enters a German university is perhaps comparable to the American college student in the middle of the sophomore year, assuming the college to be one with high academic standards, and further assuming the student to be enrolled in an arts-and-science program. There is no place in the German university system for anything like the undergraduate business courses which accommodate so many young Americans. Perhaps certain special German academies which lie outside the framework of the university system might be comparable, but as to that I have no evidence. What is relevant to my discussion in this chapter is the fact that only 7 or 8 per cent of an age group (i.e., those born in the same year) attend a German university, while something like the same percentage of an age group obtain *graduate* degrees from American universities. These highly selected groups of mature students are thus somewhat comparable. On the other hand, over 30 per cent of an age group enter an undergraduate department of a university in the United States or enter a separate four-year college. And of the bachelor degrees awarded at the end of a four-year course, about 15 per cent are given to those who have majored in business or commerce. As compared with Germany, the American system is characterized by diversity, flexibility and a total lack of uniformity as regards standards for degrees and diplomas.

Whether or not the undergraduate courses in business are still as vulnerable to criticism as two surveys, made a few years ago, indicated, I do not know. Neither in his school course nor in the university would the German encounter the kind of instruction which is given in courses often announced as elementary and advanced typewriting, radio station management, trade associations, real estate brokerage, hotel front office procedure, materials handling, closing real estate transactions, airport management, public relations correspondence, operating a small store, and freight claims procedure.

The student who enrolls in a German university and who wishes to tie his studies as closely as possible to a future business career will attend lectures on principles of business management and related topics as well as economics. He will also participate in seminars on business and economic problems. The German tradition of *Lernfreiheit* means that unlike even a graduate school of business in the United States, there will be no fixed program of studies, no courses in the American sense of the word and few examinations. When he feels ready, the student will take a set of examinations for a diploma. The model for the type of instruction has been provided by the law faculty and indeed, originally, whatever instruction was offered in applied economics was offered by the faculty of law. Conditions have been changing quickly in recent years in some universities,

I have been told, but nothing like the case method has been introduced. Therefore, even for mature, intellectually able students, one may say at the true university level, the education of the future business executives in the two countries reflects the same predilection in the two countries as does the education of lawyers. Such a contrast, I must emphasize, is quite apart from the absence in the German system of collegiate instruction in practical affairs. To consider the advantages and disadvantages of the chaotic but highly flexible American scheme, with two thousand degree-granting institutions, would take me far beyond my examination of two modes of thought. Rather, I wish to concentrate attention on a contrast between what may be called the true university function of the leading American institutions and its German equivalents.

IV

SCHOLARS, SCIENTISTS AND PHILOSOPHERS

THE UNIVERSITY is the home of the scholar, the scientist and the philosopher. Such a proposition would be accepted today as a description of the universities on both sides of the Atlantic; though Americans would wish to add that certain other classes of teachers should also be welcomed in this home. When one departs from such a very general statement and tries to be more specific in characterizing German and American universities, difficulties arise. The differences in the methods of educating future lawyers and businessmen were the subject of the last chapter. According to my view, these differences are not superficial; they reflect important characteristic outlooks, on the one hand, and to some degree determine these outlooks, on the other. If one turns to the education of future professors, scholars and scientists, one finds again great divergencies in practice and in outlook between the universities in the United States and in Germany. And with certain reservations one may say the German arrangements are characteristic for the European institutions in general. This fact makes it seem all the more strange that the American university tradition as it exists today should be so divergent from that on the continent of Europe. For it was from Europe that we in the United States less than a hundred years ago imported the idea of a university.

The divergence is far more striking today than was the case at the turn of the century. In terms of the analysis I am presenting in this volume, one may say that in the last sixty years the implications of accepting the empirical-inductive mode of thought have been developed rapidly in the United States while no comparable development has taken place as yet in the universities of Germany. What we now call the "behavioral sciences" are not recognized by any such labels across the ocean. It is difficult to find the exact German equivalent of two phrases which abound in the writings of Americans about education—"the social sciences" and "social studies." On the other hand, the words "philosophy" and "philosophic outlook" intrude themselves on every page of German discussions of German higher education. It is significant that not long ago in many German universities, all the professors concerned with scholarly activities and research in the arts and sciences were grouped in one faculty, the philosophical faculty. It is also significant that the applied natural sciences have never been taken in by German universities. During the late nineteenth century, the education of engineers was developed in separate *Technische Hochschulen,* which, however, eventually were given the same status as a university. This historic fact emphasizes the reluctance of the German professor to be concerned with the direct training for the professions—a reluctance which I attempted to spell out in the last chapter.

Superficially the greatest difference between higher education on the continent of Europe and in the United States is the total absence of the equivalent of a four-year undergraduate course the other side of the Atlantic. As far as Germany is concerned, one might say that the first two years of an American four-year college or undergraduate course could be comparable to the last year of the Gymnasium. I write "could be" because, of course, there is no uniformity in the United States as to what a college student studies in the freshman or sophomore years. At all events, the absence in Europe of the equivalent of the American college as an intermediary between school and a university (in the European sense) has had important consequences. Or rather one might say the existence of the American college and the enormous expansion in the numbers attending these institutions has profoundly affected the attitude of American universities toward the newer social sciences of psychology, sociology and anthropology.

Turn back the pages of history sixty years and we note two important changes which have occurred: one, the diminution in the relative significance for *undergraduates* of the study of philosophy, and the other, the vast increase in the number of professors of the newer social sciences. Typical of the changes I have in mind is the fact that William James—the author of a famous book on psychology—was a professor of philosophy at Harvard. Sixty years ago it was the group of philosophy professors in the same institution whose courses were considered the most significant by those undergraduates seeking what we now call a general education. Today the same type of individual would, more often than not, be found concentrating his attention on the study of psychology and sociology—two fields of study not formally recognized in Harvard College in 1904. With the vast increase in undergraduate enrollments has come a vast increase in the size of the instructing staffs in all the social sciences, but the most striking change has been in the fields of the newer social sciences, whose existence was hardly recognized sixty years ago. There can be no doubt that these sciences, which are predominantly taught by professors with an empirical-inductive outlook, have proved extremely popular to the American undergraduate.

Increased demand for staff in undergraduate institutions has led to increased numbers in the graduate schools of arts and sciences working for a Ph.D. in psychology and sociology (and to a lesser extent anthropology). The expansion of the field of psychology at both the undergraduate and graduate levels has been particularly striking. Closely related has been the growth of various phases of educational psychology and the increasing importance of this wide field in the education of teachers and others concerned with our schools. Similar developments have been conspicuous by their absence in German universities. I have heard it said, by one in a position to know, that there is today in the Federal Republic of Germany no laboratory for experimental animal psychology, and few professors are equipped to evaluate the experimentation which has led to the new developments in teaching machines and programed instruction.

The whole method of instruction and particularly of examination of future teachers for the Gymnasiums is so different from our methods in the graduate schools of arts and sciences that a comparison of German and American education is almost impossible at this level (or at any other, for that matter). Nevertheless I venture the generalization that the status of the newer social sciences in Germany and the United States is quite different. One can attribute this difference to the far-reaching influence of the great German philosophic tradition. And this is the usual explanation. Without denying the importance of this tradition and its influence on all aspects of German life, I nevertheless venture to attribute great influence to the professors of law and the attitudes of these professors in the United States on the one hand and Germany on the other.

I should be overstating my case if I argued that the commitment of American professors to the case method had been a powerful influence in favor of the expansion of the newer social sciences. But at least there has been little resistance to such expansion by the law faculty. While on the other hand, in German universities it is generally conceded that the law faculties on the whole have been both very powerful and highly conservative. (Because of the organization of the university, the attitude of members of one faculty has had far more effect on other faculties than is the case in the United States.) One might say that the powerful professors of the social sciences in a German university had been social philosophers—for the most part professors of jurisprudence. They had accepted as colleagues professors of history and even of economics and perhaps of political sciences if this subject was treated from a broad point of view and if the generalizations were historically based and of wide applicability.

To illustrate the antithesis I have been developing, let me refer the reader to a book by the eminent contemporary German philosopher Karl Jaspers, entitled *The Idea of the University*. At one point, the contrast is made between "practical instruction" in a "particular skill required for a particular occupation," and "scientific instruction." The latter, we are told, "seeks to guide us to the foundations of all knowledge by the light of the idea of unity." [1] The author freely admits that the German university today is hardly more than an aggregate of professional training schools, yet he insists that there must be a scientific basis for each of these schools, else the university would disintegrate; a university stands for a wholeness of knowledge, which means a unity of science. The word "science," of course, in German is *Wissenschaft,* which covers the whole field of scholarly endeavors that we might

---

[1] Karl Jaspers. *The Idea of the University*. Boston: Beacon Press, 1959, p. 80.

define as the search for truth. It is broader than our word "science" in that it includes theology, medicine, law, philosophy, philology, as well as the academic disciplines we name as the natural and social sciences. It is a word with a broader meaning but also a narrower meaning, and this narrower meaning, I believe, is related to the German's predilection for theoretical speculation and deductive reasoning. The European in general and the German in particular has his learned eyes fixed on general principles. Unless he can find these principles in a field of study, he is loath to give to the inquiry scientific status. He is unwilling to admit the teachers and students of the field to a university.

If there are no general principles, the subject is not scientific; if it is not scientific, it does not belong in a university; the very essence of a university is at stake in such a matter, so argued one German professor of economics to me in deadly earnest. Let it be noted that he did not object to the case method of studying business administration because the subject was too practical. Law, an applied social science, is one of the oldest and most honored of the learned professions in Europe. No, it is not the use to which the knowledge is to be put which is at issue. What is at issue is a judgment about the nature of the corpus of knowledge which is to be transmitted. A university professor, many a European would say, must be concerned with something more than sets of rules or packages of recipes; there must be broad general principles. And if pressed as to why there must be such principles, the answer would probably be to the effect that otherwise there can be no real university instruction. For a university, as contrasted with a trade school, the European would say, is concerned with the kind of instruction which develops a competence based on what I have designated as deductive reasoning. Such knowledge enables a practitioner to solve problems by deductions to meet specific situations. He is able to reason as to what should be done by starting with certain wide generalizations or accepted premises. In a belligerent mood, a European would argue that just passing on a set of recipes is a business of a school for technicians, mechanics or hotel chefs. And even you Americans don't award a Ph.D. in cookery, he might add!

The words I have just put in the mouth of the European critic raise a question which many Americans have raised now and again about specific programs of instruction. Many professors in one faculty or department have severely criticized the courses offered by professors in another faculty or department along the lines I have just suggested. I seem to remember that, as a university president, I used to hear such comments from time to time. It would be impolitic for me to try and remember which faculty was most criticized. But leaving campus warfare aside, it is interesting to note that some Americans have used phrases similar to those used by European critics. Those who were attacked, it was claimed, were either teaching only a set of common-sense rules or else dressing up empirical observations in pompous language. I recall one professor of political science in the European tradition dismissing the work of a colleague as the equivalent of studying city government by counting the manhole covers in the sewer system.

The issue involved in the Germans' resistance to the admission of certain types of instruction into the sacred precincts of their universities thus transcends national boundaries. In this country, since our use of the word "university" is very different from that of the European, the issue must be rephrased. The question, it seems to me, is as follows: At what level of instruction and in what type of American academic organization should instruction be provided in those practical fields where admittedly there are few if any general principles? Thus stated, the issue involves far more than the social sciences. In the practical arts related to the natural sciences, it involves a consideration of the difference between training technicians and training members of a profession. It further involves a detailed analysis of the programs of instruction in the various branches of technology, of engineering, of applied biology including agriculture and of medicine. As an ideal, one might postulate that those who have the kind of academic talent which enables them to grasp readily general principles and to think in abstract terms should devote their time beyond the high school to mastering general principles. Such people should be exposed as little as possible to the process of learning specific rules and technical procedures. The whole development of education in technology and medicine has been in this direction.

I venture to remind the reader of what I have written in Chapter I. The sciences of physics, chemistry and biology today have developed to a point where a theoretical framework is at hand to which many of the advanced practices in the practical arts may be readily related. These practical fields, too, have developed their own conceptual schemes which supplement the limited rules and generalizations that we often call "purely empirical." The theoretical component of the corpus of knowledge available to the metallurgist, for example, is now extensive, though not as large, perhaps, as that available to the electrical engineer. On the other hand, those concerned with certain fields of applied chemistry, such as the manufacture of leather, must still rely largely on a mass of empirical rules—the theoretical component in this ancient art is still relatively small. Within the areas of the applied physical and biological sciences, with some exceptions, it is not too difficult today to identify a body of general principles which can be used as a basis for advanced instruction. What still remains from the days when these practical arts were largely empirical can be taught either by the apprentice system or to those who will terminate their education at the level we call the training of technicians.

When we turn to the practical arts involved with human affairs, we find it far more difficult to sort out the limited rules and factual information from the general principles. This is why the German professors take such a dim view of certain aspects of American education and why we find a running criticism even by Americans of the content of many courses in business, commerce, journalism and education. There exists a mass of practical "know-how" in all these areas which is the result of countless trial-and-error procedures by practitioners of the art. To what degree can such material form the basis for formal instruction at the college or university level? To what degree should the "know-how" be imparted by the apprentice system? These seem to me the basic issues which underlie much of the controversy about the academic standing of the work in the applied social sciences; a similar controversy is involved in appraising the instruction provided in schools of education.

The situation is further complicated by the fact that a practitioner of an art involving human beings may be guided by deduction from two somewhat different types of generalizations. One is strictly analogous to the generalization of those who are dealing with inanimate nature. The other is represented by the legal norms of which Professor Redlich wrote. The judge in seeking a rule of law is concerned with deductive reasoning which starts from certain wide premises whose validity is not generally believed to rest on experimentation. The engineer as a practitioner in contrast is concerned with deductions from empirical rules or scientific generalizations, which do depend on experimentation. So, too, is the physician as regards most of his decisions. But the physician is also well aware of a set of normative principles which affect his behavior. These are embodied in the code of medical ethics and certain parts of the legal code. What a physician *ought* to do in a given situation is determined largely by the current scientific knowledge but also to a degree by deductions from ethical or legal principles.

The wide generalizations from which the judge starts his chain of reasoning differ from the wide generalizations of the engineer for several reasons. In the first place, the one concerns human behavior and the welfare of society, the other inanimate nature. To my mind, however, the more fundamental difference is to be found by noting the history of the generalizations and estimating the probability of their change. The change from the practical arts with their narrower generalizations to the applied sciences with their wider principles is a matter of a few centuries; within the memory of an applied scientist, drastic changes in his body of knowledge have occurred. In contrast, basic legal principles change very slowly. If they did not, "going to law" would be even more of an uncertain business than it is. Perhaps a layman might suggest that the conflict at present among legal scholars as to the nature of the law turns on this very question, namely, how rapidly and by what means do legal premises become altered? One might say that the engineer expects the basic principles of his craft to change and that innovations will be accepted because deductions from them accord with repeated experiments and observations. In spite of Judge Cardozo's statement quoted in the last chapter, judges in general, particularly in Europe, do not expect the basic principles of their craft to change.

Are all generalizations in the social sciences comparable to the norms of law? Obviously not. The newer social sciences are involved in the process of expanding narrow generalizations about human beings by the empirical-inductive approach. As a goal the practitioners hope to develop a fabric of theory strictly comparable to that which encompasses the premises of the modern metallurgist and engineer. In other words, what seems to separate the two lines of argument used by the judge, on the one hand, and the engineer, on the other, turns on the way the basic principles have evolved and how the practitioner regards them. Today, in the affairs of man, the only clearly recognizable wide generalizations are those which, like the legal ones, have an ancient history. Those who prefer the theoretical-deductive approach naturally turn to their study. But before I pursue such scholarly activities further, let me return to my discussion, in the preceding chapter, of the case method in instructing lawyers and businessmen. For it might now appear that while the two methods are similar pedagogic devices, the principles that are discovered by the students for themselves (or so it is alleged) are so different as to fall into separate categories.

First of all, it is important to note that the case materials used by the law schools and the business schools are very different. The law student is sent to read the decisions of judges which are available as official printed documents. This is the same material to which the practitioner refers constantly in preparing arguments, at least in common-law countries, where previous decisions of the judges play so large a part. In contrast to the law libraries stand the shelves of a business school, stocked for the most part with books published by professors about economics and all its phases and about business practices.

When the case method of studying business was started, the necessary material did not exist. It has been built up slowly and published as a result of a vast amount of labor. Indeed, we are told in the Harvard report of 1954, to which I have already referred, that the Harvard Business School's "Collection of empirical case materials kept constantly abreast of new developments in business represents a cumulative expenditure estimated at two and a half million dollars."

At this point I must return briefly to the law and underline the obvious fact that the rules of law are enforced by agents of society. If one violates them, one risks having a sanction applied. This is true also of a code of ethics. The famous Hippocratic Oath taken by members of the medical profession prescribes what a physician ought and ought not to do. Violation of the principles of such a code involves the risk of having agents of the organized profession apply sanctions against the violator. The trivial example of a member of a club being forced to resign because of repeated violation of some rule belongs in the same category with the example of a person being fined or punished or deprived of a right by a court order. In the legal case, the judge may apply the most careful logical chain of reasoning and start from a wide generalization, whereas a club rule is clearly the narrowest of generalizations. Therefore, the kind of consequences involved in legal matters which are called applying a sanction are quite apart from the width of the generalizations from which the deductive line of reasoning starts.

The businessman, we may imagine, starts his line of reasoning from some principle he learned through the case method which exemplified the consequences of certain types of actions in certain situations. He argues deductively, as does the judge, or the executive committee of the club considering the expulsion of a member, and comes to specific conclusions he believes to correspond to the decision he must make. The decision is made but not enforced by society or the action of a group (a profession or a club); indeed, one can hardly say it is enforced at all. A sequence of events follows which the businessman regards as favorable or unfavorable to his enterprise, and after the lapse of minutes, hours, days, months or even years, he concludes in retrospect his decision had been right. The interactions of other personalities play a large part in the events; otherwise the whole decision-making process, I suggest, is parallel to a man manipulating nature. The steelmaker who decides to heat his furnace to such and such a temperature, or add so many tons of such material, must likewise allow a lapse of time before learning whether his decision had been right (was the product as he desired?). The principle from which the steelmaker starts his chain of reasoning is today a result of centuries of practical experience with a strong theoretical component.

The businessman, unlike the judge, must constantly

make decisions which cannot be isolated but on the contrary are enmeshed in a net of complications. Only when one element of the web can be isolated is it possible for these practitioners of applied social science to start with certain principles or generalizations and run through a line of deductive reasoning. Usually there are many lines of argument which run together and at times become entangled. The same is true of decisions made by all of us in everyday affairs. The vast number of our day-to-day decisions could, if we stopped to think, be found to be based on common-sense generalizations about the behavior of human beings. They are predictive generalizations, but narrow and unconnected by any theoretical fabric. We have vast knowledge of the way sane, sober people are likely to behave under a variety of circumstances. When, for example, a person is asked a question, or subjected to a threat, or confronted with a danger to life or limb, we are quite confident in predicting the behavior. Indeed, if the behavior is far removed from our expectation, we can say with certainty that the person is reacting abnormally; we must either call in a psychiatrist or put the drunk to bed, as the case may be.

All this common-sense knowledge about people seems to me analogous to the recipes of the artisans of whom I have written earlier. The study of business by the case method *coupled* with the advances in the sciences of psychology, sociology and anthropology is in process of widening the common-sense generalizations basic to normal human behavior. All of which, it is quite clear, is in the empirical-inductive tradition.

But surely, besides the legal norms, there are broad general principles, wide generalizations which bear on human conduct; so many a reader will maintain. I agree; it seems quite clear that few, if any, people can carry on their lives without accepting some theoretical framework into which common-sense narrow generalizations must be fitted. At this point we meet the philosopher again. Or perhaps I should say that the American college student *ought* to meet the philosopher and the German university student is *supposed* to have such an encounter. Indeed, the word *Weltanschauung* has come to epitomize the outlook of those who demand an all-embracing answer to the deep problems of human life and the nature of the cosmos. The theoretical-deductive mode of thought merges with the speculative or even the fantastic when one steps into this area of expression. For those whose education has been such as to emphasize the empirical-inductive mode of thinking, a study of the writings of the famous philosophers may be the only serious exposure to the other manner of thought. This is why philosophy as an academic discipline is so important. Unless one has wrestled with problems of epistemology and ontology, it is easy to succumb to the temptation to accept at face value those high-sounding pseudo-philosophic ideas which are always current.

I doubt if anyone will challenge the statement that the influence of the German philosophic tradition which starts with Kant is less than it was two or three generations ago. Indeed, in the United States it is hard to find, today, admirers of the writings of Hegel, and most people have forgotten, if they ever knew, that John Dewey started as an Hegelian. The retreat of systematic philosophy has paralleled the advance of the natural sciences. And there have been those who believed that the construction of a scientific world view was an inevitable substitute for one or the other of the older philosophic systems of thought. But those who interpret modern science as do Quine and Kuhn cannot, as I explained in the first chapter, find an ultimate answer to the riddle of the universe in the theories of the natural scientists. Nor can they look forward to such answers from the social scientists, even on the optimistic assumption that the behavioral sciences develop in the next hundred years as did chemistry and physics in the nineteenth century.

Those who demand certainty in a secular world view can turn to the natural sciences only if they accept something approaching Peirce's position. As I have indicated elsewhere (*Modern Science and Modern Man*. New York: Columbia University Press, 1952), I do not think modern science can be of much service to those in search of the minimal postulates required to systematize the apparently self-evident assumptions about human conduct. If I am right, then those who wish to step outside the framework of a set of religious dogmas must be prepared to relinquish the quest for certainty and universality. No one can free himself completely from the consequences of his past exposure to those metaphysical ideas which are a part of the tradition of his family and community. Each person who seeks to detach himself from the dogmas will have a different degree of attachment to the different parts of the entire scheme. Therefore, as I see it, the search for the minimal commitments on which to construct a "philosophy of life" must be both highly personal and continually provisional. The process will in all probability be different for those who prefer the empirical-inductive mode of thought and those who feel more at home in the theoretical-deductive tradition.

Needless to say, a vast library could be filled with learned discussions of the search for the wide generalizations from which one may start a line of reasoning and end with a decision of what a person believes is right. The conflicts between such conclusions and those arrived at by agents of a community who interpret a legal or a professional code are the basis of the tragedies of life. The dilemmas of the abolitionist after the Dred Scott decision of the Supreme Court is a classical example for an American who is willing to think deeply about our past. Is there a higher law than that laid down by the Supreme Court of the United States? If so, how is one to find it? Whose interpretation will one take? The legal scholars, particularly on the Continent, who have sought for a natural law have been repeatedly answered by other scholars, who have pointed to the lack of agreement as to the principles of the natural law. Furthermore, the critics of the idea of a natural law have emphasized the difficulty of expressing general principles in sufficiently clear terms to allow these principles to serve as premises for a logical deductive argument. The problems presented by the commandment "Thou shalt not kill" as a premise for deductive reasoning in time of war has been repeatedly pointed out by both believers and nonbelievers.

The great religious systems of the world are systems into which many of the narrow common-sense generalizations have been fitted, particularly those which may be formulated in terms of what a person ought to do. Saints and prophets have thus approached the problems of human behavior from a theoretical-deductive standpoint. The Judaic-Christian tradition as it has developed to the present day, quite apart from metaphysical and theological considerations, includes wide generalizations which almost all of us accept as a matter of course. Let me call them wide premises of our cultural pattern. From them one can try and deduce by a chain of logical reasoning consequences applicable to specific situations. For a vast number of people a determination of what they think people ought to do is arrived at in this manner. The legal norms of which Professor Redlich speaks would seem to fall into the same category as the other wide premises from which people tend to argue when they speak in ethical terms.

One example of a comprehensive theoretical frame of reference for the social sciences is the official dogmas of communism generally known as the principles of dialectical materialism. As has been pointed out by many people, here we find a religion without a theology and without reference to supernatural events or sanctions. Here is a system which rejoices the heart of those who incline to the theoretical-deductive approach to human problems but who repudiate the Judaic-Christian tradition. As Professor Michael Polanyi has pointed out in his brilliant essay on "The Magic of Marxism," the assertions of the high priests of communism are accepted because they claim to satisfy certain moral passions and are alleged to be scientific.

"The propagandistic appeal of Marxism is the most interesting case of what might be called the moral force of immorality," he writes. "For it is the most precisely formulated system having such a paradoxical appeal and this self-contradiction actually seems to supply the main impulse of the Marxist movement . . . it enables the modern mind, tortured by moral self-doubt, to indulge its moral passions in terms which also satisfy its passion for ruthless objectivity." Thus, it is a combination of crusading zeal of the nineteenth-century liberals with the demands for certainty in a science of society which have eventuated in communistic dogmas.

It is quite beyond the scope of this volume to attempt to summarize the principles of dialectical materialism and expose the fallacies inherent in this set of dogmas. One might point out, however, that like all religions, communism has known heresy, heresy-hunting and changes of position by those who sit in the seats of power and thus control orthodoxy. And I need not point out the practical consequences of living in a totalitarian state with an *all-embracing* official dogma. A peep over the wall that divides Berlin will provide evidence to indicate why at the risk of life and limb so many Germans fled from east to west. Whether or not the acceptance of dialectical materialism as a philosophic system is bound to lead to totalitarian states may be argued, though I am inclined to think social, political and intellectual regimentation is a necessary consequence of the belief that there is only one set of premises from which one may proceed to deduce conclusions about the way human beings behave and ought to behave.

Evidence for the view I have just presented can be found by reading the writings of officials of the so-called German Democratic Republic (the regime in the Soviet Zone of Occupation). Even a superficial study of the books and magazine articles that have been published in the Soviet Zone and East Berlin in the last twenty years highlights the dangers inherent in a complete devotion to the theoretical-deductive mode of thought. If it is assumed that the theoretical fabric is complete and all human problems can be solved by logical reference to this fabric, these dissenters are worse than heretics; they are unscientific! It can be argued that such people are like the uneducated who might claim the earth is flat. In no country in the world would a teacher be allowed, today, to question the statement that we live on the surface of a globe. In the same way, so many Communists would argue, we cannot tolerate in our teachers or among our own writers anyone who questions the scientific basis of dialectical materialism. But when one examines the details of this all-embracing theoretical fabric, differences of opinion soon arise. And here we meet a difficulty inherent in the theoretical-deductive approach to the social sciences. What sorts of evidence are to be permitted in a consideration of differences of opinion among those who expound the details of the scientific theory? Are the consequences of one view or another to be examined by noting what has occurred in the past? Or will one put the two views to a test by noting what happens in the future? To go down either of these roads, however, is to contaminate the purity of the theoretical-deductive mode of thought. As applied to dialectical materialism, it is to question the completeness of the doctrines as set forth in the writings of Marx, Lenin and their followers. The political consequences of deviationism are well known to all who have followed the course of history the other side of the iron curtain.

The heresies within the Communist world illustrate the difficulties of getting agreement on the details of a theoretical framework which is all-embracing and is unconnected with observation and experiment. One sees the difficulty when one examines much less ambitious attempts than dialectical materialism. One sees dangers in certain theories of social science in non-communistic societies. The danger is that vague general statements which carry emotional overtones are mistaken for elements of a theory which is designed to serve the social sciences as does the fabric of modern natural science. The scholars who labor in this field, be they theologians, or philosophers of law or of ethics, or political scientists, or even economists, are always facing the danger of lack of precision if they reach for wide comprehension. More often than not they are forced into narrow generalizations and thus end by having to operate on what is essentially a purely empirical basis.

The dangers of those who advance the social sciences from the empirical-inductive standpoint are quite different. In the first place, if the history of the biological and physical sciences be relevant, there must be a jump from time to time to generalizations not as yet warranted by any evidence. Yet to fashion a generalization from which deductions can be made which are subject to check has proved a matter of great difficulty (as has been the case in the natural sciences in the more distant past). So far no great advances in this direction have been made except perhaps by Freud in psychology and by a few economists, though even in these cases I have many reservations. Experimental psychology gives great promise; if and when it develops further, it may play the same role in the practice of teaching that microbiology played in the practice of medicine after Pasteur's discoveries to which I referred in the opening chapter.

The second danger which confronts the empirical social scientists today and leads to that suspicion of his work by Europeans on which I have dwelt, perhaps too much, is that it is far too easy to discover narrow generalizations. Research can lead to a series of unconnected trivialities. This is true in the natural sciences, it is only fair to point out; but these trivialities are buried under the successful forward movement in our day of the combined inductive-deductive approach. But the trivialities of research in the social sciences stand out for all to see. One has only to read the list of titles of the doctors' theses in the empirical social science fields, including education, to realize how much wasted time and effort may be involved in purely empirical research. To be sure, it is no different from stamp collecting, but as yet not even an American university has awarded a doctor's degree for success in this widespread activity.

As a pedagogic device, the empirical-inductive approach has proved its worth whether one is interested in discovering legal norms or in discovering rather narrow generalizations used as premises by businessmen struggling with their problems. Contrasts can be made between wide premises from which legal and ethical decisions are often derived and those limited practical rules of predicting human behavior. Yet, in spite of this apparent dichotomy, the advances in the theory and practice of all the sciences and all the practical arts (including the arts of educating practitioners) I believe will be made in the future as in the past by a combination of the empirical-inductive with the theoretical-deductive mode of thought.

IN CONCLUSION

AN INDUSTRIALIZED free society needs two types of individuals reconciled with each other. The one type prefers the theoretical-deductive approach to problems, the other the empirical-inductive. The reconciliation of these two types, I have attempted to demonstrate, is essential for the continuation of a free society in an age of science and technology. This is my Credo. It remains for me in a few concluding pages to show the educational implications of this Credo. For it is through education that a modern society develops the talent which is needed. The needs of an open society today, if it is to continue secure, prosperous and open, are, in terms of developed talent, of a different order of magnitude from the needs of a free nation a century ago. This fact is what has led to such a deep concern with schools and universities in many countries. Let me now attempt to show the relevance of my analysis to the current vigorous debate about education.

I have written about the preference of individuals for one manner of thinking or another. It seems clear that for the majority of intellectually able youth the mode of thought they will prefer in later life is determined largely by education. There are probably, however, in every thousand such youths in each generation, a few in whom the tendency of which I write is so marked that it would be almost impossible for them to operate successfully in the other mode. The best example is provided, perhaps, by potential creative mathematicians or by potential experimental geniuses. If my diagnosis is correct, the educational system of a free nation will perform its function successfully to the extent that the talents of the few whose potentialities are clearly marked at a young age are rapidly developed to the full.

In the natural sciences, pure and applied, as the situation now stands, the needs for the two approaches are clearly recognized. For example, for many years, the departments of chemistry in large universities have sought to have both experimentalists and theoreticians among their members. The same is true in many industrial laboratories. And since the need for imaginative, able men committed to both modes of thought is recognized, the educational processes in the natural sciences, including mathematics, now endeavor to develop both types of talent. There is no need to labor this point as far as the natural sciences and technology are concerned. The case is quite different as regards the social sciences and the education of practitioners in human affairs, including teachers.

If what I have written in the preceding chapter has any merit, those concerned with educating future men of affairs and training social scientists need to recognize the twofold need and provide appropriate educational channels. There should be places within the whole range of the offerings of a university for those who from early youth desire to study human problems by empirical methods and also places for those who are interested only in broad speculative theories. The ratio of out-and-out empiricists to devoted theoreticians may well vary from field to field, but there should be at least a few of each in the social sciences and in the humanities in every university.

I have written about the few whose predisposition is manifested early. The vast majority of capable college young people interested in human affairs are not likely to be heavily committed to either mode of thought. Therefore, one of the problems facing an academic community is the emphasis to be placed on the one approach or the other. A shift of emphasis will produce large effects on the attitudes of those who are being educated as lawyers, as businessmen, as journalists, as teachers, as social scientists. It would be presumptuous of me to suggest to what extent there is need of correcting the present balance in each of these educational programs in any given nation. But I am sufficiently convinced of the necessity of a balance between the two modes of thought to be quite certain that in every phase of university work in every country there should be a constant examination of the situation.

The history of the natural sciences shows that it is possible for many able men to operate effectively in both modes of thought. And as far as the practitioners are concerned, there is ample evidence to indicate that a person may shift from one approach to the other. While such people may not either produce the most original and profound generalizations or be the most productive investigators, I am convinced that they have a highly important part to play in the modern world. One of the tasks of the universities is to provide the intellectual and emotional nourishment for such men. To this end it is imperative that the strong proponents of the two modes of thought in the social sciences develop a tolerant attitude to each other. In the past the tendency of the empiricists to dismiss the writings of all theoreticians as meaningless nonsense, and the tendency of all theoreticians to talk as though all empirical research were beneath contempt, has polarized the total academic world as regards both research and education. In the social sciences and the education of practitioners, attitudes similar to that of Clerk Maxwell toward Bell have been extremely prevalent. Between faculties, and sometimes within faculties, hostility has developed between those committed to the one approach or the other. Under such conditions, the balance I write of is unlikely to be attained, and few if any students will develop the readiness to think in either the one mode or the other as circumstances may determine.

While I am pleading for more mutual respect between professors of different temperaments, I must also plead for many rigorous criticisms of the publications of both kinds of scholars. And I am inclined to think such criticism is most likely to be effective if it comes from those who recognize the validity of both modes of thought. The trivial nature and limitations of much of the research of the American social sciences are all too infrequently pointed out. Most of the theses presented for a doctor's degree in some fields would be best left at least unpublished, if not unwritten. On the other hand, some of the writings of German scholars need as a counterbalance critical comments from those who are not emotionally committed to the theoretical-deductive mode of thought. Education in Germany, in my opinion, suffers from neglect of the results of empirical research, particularly that of the experimental psychologists. In short, there should be on both sides of the Atlantic, I venture to suggest, more frequent encounters between those who approach human problems from widely different viewpoints. At present the members of each camp direct their writings largely to their fellow campmates and dismiss with scorn what is published by all others.

To the extent that universities and learned societies are able today to be concerned with the development of the social sciences as a whole (as apart from training practitioners), those who determine policy should have a double aim. The mutual respect between empiricist and theoretician should be developed, and at the same time ruthless criticism should be encouraged. At least, this is my firm conviction. I recognize the difficulty of reconciling the two aims. But I suggest the recognition of the two modes of thought may help in such endeavors. Just as a man needs two legs to walk on, the social sciences need two types of thinkers if the advance is, as it should be, to meet the needs of a free and highly industrialized society.

BIBLIOGRAPHY

BUTTERFIELD, H. *The Origins of Modern Science, 1300–1800*. London: G. Bell and Sons, Ltd., 1949.

CARDOZO, BENJAMIN N. *The Nature of the Judicial Process*. New Haven: Yale University Press, 1921.

COHEN, MORRIS R., and NAGEL, ERNEST. *An Introduction to Logic and Scientific Method*. New York: Harcourt, Brace & Company, 1934.

CONANT, JAMES BRYANT. *Science and Common Sense*. New Haven: Yale University Press, 1951.

——— (ed.). *Case Histories in Experimental Science*. 2 vols. Cambridge, Mass.: Harvard University Press, 1957.

DUPREE, A. HUNTER. *Asa Gray, 1810–1888*. Cambridge, Mass.: Belknap Press of Harvard University Press, 1959.

KUHN, THOMAS S. *The Structure of Scientific Revolutions*. Chicago: University of Chicago Press, 1962.

LURIE, EDWARD. *Louis Agassiz: A Life in Science*. Chicago: University of Chicago Press, 1960.

MACMILLAN (HUGH PATTISON), LORD. "Two Ways of Thinking." Rede Lecture, Cambridge University, 1934.

PEPPER, STEPHEN C. *Ethics*. New York: Appleton-Century-Crofts, 1960.

REDLICH, PROF. JOSEPH. "The Case Method in American Law Schools," *Bulletin No. 8* of the Carnegie Foundation for the Advancement of Teaching. New York, 1914.

SCHLESINGER, ARTHUR M., JR., and WHITE, MORTON M. *Paths of American Thought*. Boston: Houghton Mifflin Co., 1963. (See in particular Chapters 9, 10, 11, 15, 23, and 24.)